TEILHARD DE CHARDIN

TEILHARD
DE
CHARDIN

A Critical Study

by OLIVIER RABUT, O.P.

SHEED AND WARD — NEW YORK

LIBRARY OF CONGRESS CATALOG CARD NUMBER 61-11794

MANUFACTURED IN THE UNITED STATES OF AMERICA

ABBREVIATIONS

A   *L'Apparition de l'Homme*, Éditions du Seuil, 1956

G   *Le Groupe zoologique humain*, Albin Michel, 1956

M   *Le Milieu divin*, Collins, 1960 (Harpers, 1960)

P   *The Phenomenon of Man*, Collins, 1960 (Harpers, 1959)

V   *Le Vision du passé*, Éditions du Seuil, 1957

Grateful acknowledgment is hereby made to Harper & Brothers for quotations from *The Phenomenon of Man* and *The Divine Milieu* by Teilhard de Chardin.

CONTENTS

INTRODUCTION
THE INVITATION TO SCIENCE

NEVER, up to the twentieth century, has there been any phenomenon to compare with modern science. Now, at last, men have found a common ground on which to meet, and exact findings over which they can agree. It does not take two scientists long to understand each other, even if they are of different nationalities; they may not have any language in common, or be able to exchange two words with each other; but one of them has only to scribble an outline or jot down an equation, and the other can follow him, interested in his train of thought and able to correct any hasty slip that he may make. At a deeper level, both are involved in a general movement of minds—a movement greater than any individual taking part in it, but one that can find use for all, sweep all along on its broad current. "The modern idea of the atom belongs at this moment, *communally*, to a few thousand physicists, *without being thought in its totality by any one of them*."[1] Ideas of great

[1] *A*, 337, *n. 2.*
1*

value, embryonic as yet, are, through collective effort, taking shape, growing, developing. Once a trend of this sort has been seen and felt, it becomes doubtful whether anything intellectually or spiritually fructifying can exist outside it. Yet the trend is not immediately apparent, and there are many—including those with technical knowledge—who are unaware of it. Then, one day, realization dawns, and we are swept on by a kind of gulf-stream of quite unsuspected strength.

The mind is at last growing up. It has come to know its own powers, and see that it is working to renew the face of the earth; of all our former ideas, ways of life, and deeply personal and individual approaches to life, nothing will ever be as it was before. Pierre Termier speaks of the "youthful vapours" which transformed the sedimentary rocks, and one feels that something of the same sort is happening now in the case of man. A group of men, increasing in number every year, has made two discoveries— the discovery of its own youthfulness, and the discovery of some first beginning of certainty. It is the spirit of youth, allied with the critical mind. There is a dawning hope of forming some concept of the objective world—not, doubtless, of ever finding the full explanation of it (many scientists have grown fairly humble over this point), but of attaining a progressive knowledge, based at last on sure methods.

A new culture is taking shape, one open to the masses, and fitting in with the natural movement of the mind. Social classes, different races, all unite in one vision. Levels of intelligence vary, of course, and there will always be the great aristocrats of thought; but their superiority is now beyond dispute; it is something that everyone acknowledges, and that wrongs no one, for it means only that they are further ahead than the rest of us along the same road.

There will, of course, be those who point out the limitations of science. Science does not explain everything: it can never take the place of morality. Its supporters are often lacking in philosophical depth; often, too, they have no sense of the spiritual, and it is simply their own obtuseness that makes them think they have solved the real problems. Science is not a humanism. Has it really, up to now, thrown any light on the problem of living—the only problem that in fact exists? Even within its own sphere of competence, it speaks with an uncertain voice; one theory succeeds and disproves another.

It is easy to find an answer to the last objection. All the true acquisitions of science remain. Relativity, the quantum theory, wave mechanics —all these retain whatever element of truth there was in Newtonian physics, whose validity we have now set in its right perspective and defined even though we have gone beyond it. Underlying the contemporary disputes between the various schools, we can see, if we will but look, evidence which is common to all of them —or which has at least a bearing on all of them. Thus, Teilhard de Chardin shows us the almost universal application of the transformist theory; and when he writes at such length about the "tree of life", he is only describing what every naturalist thinks today.[1]

As to the limitations of science, these vanish if, with Teilhard, we seek for a *hyperphysics*— that is, a branch of science which reflects on its own results in order to find their true import— a science which learns the total lesson of its discoveries. Physics may be described as the "systematic understanding of the whole of nature", including thought.[2] The idea of a generalized physics goes back at least as far as Aristotle. It does, of course, raise questions which I shall try to note. At least it must be accepted as a scheme, to be followed up as far as possible. In this matter there was, no doubt, considerable timidity and incompetence over the last hundred years; scientists learnt to distrust what they slightingly referred to as "metaphysics"—a form of speculation that was far too much a matter of words, too uncertain, and lacking in objective discipline. (We shall, however, be using the word with another meaning.) This is why

[1] *P*, 137 ff. The extrapolations which follow are of course more open to question.
[2] *V*, 228.

scientists so often confine themselves within narrow technical bounds; and why, when they overstep them, the results are not always too happy.[1] Warned by these failures, our contemporaries, or those who come after us, may, if they have sufficient wisdom and acceptance of reality, take on the harder task.

A general observation strikes us—namely, the strong resemblance that exists between the research of scientists in their various disciplines, and the trends of modern thought in non-scientific spheres. The two have many related themes; and concern for the right method often leads to considerable similarity of mental outlook. This suggests that syntheses may be possible, without causing any break in the mind's movement. Let us, to save time, confine ourselves to three points where this convergence may be seen.

(1) *Study confined to phenomena*, or taking phenomena as the starting-point, to provide a firm basis on which to stand. There is a careful scrutiny of the phenomenal datum—i.e., of that which is perceptible, irrespective of theoretical interpretation. In other words, the experimental datum can be examined technically to an advanced degree, without the intervention of

[1] To take only one example, I feel that Lecomte de Noüy, competent as he is in the scientific field, would have done well to stay there. When he touches on philosophical problems, he misunderstands their nature.

any postulate alien to science. Whatever the underlying philosophical problems may be, we can arrive at quite certain results as regards spontaneous functionings and the development of facts. Husserl, by reason of his methodology, refuses to pronounce on the nature of knowledge, or even on the existence of the object; but he studies human thought in its workings, and, by carefully defining the implications of the experimental fact, does indeed reach conclusions which attain the status of metaphysical problems. Teilhard takes science, and science alone, as his starting-point; he lists and groups the elements that can be tested by experiment, elements perceptible to man, taking note of the manner in which they appear to us; he refuses to leave the realm of phenomena. He tries, for instance, to define, on the level of appearances, the emergence of human intelligence, setting aside the question—on which science is incapable of pronouncing—of an ontological discontinuity; but, when he looks for the significance of all this, the conclusions he reaches fall within the field of philosophy. Thus he interprets the rise of consciousness as the axis of cosmic advance, sees it as an unswerving progress to the Omega-Point, and thereby deduces this point's pre-existence. We shall later examine the validity of such reasoning, and especially the validity of his transition from the observed fact to the significance seen in it. But in any case the method of enquiry is interesting. It may be regarded as the method of the twentieth century, for in earlier centuries it was almost unknown, whereas today it is adopted deliberately and often to the exclusion of any other.

(2) *Attention to developments*—in other words, to the part played by time. Hegel's dominant thought was the advance of history, in which he saw the groping ascent of reality, seeking self-awareness through the human mind, and trying to attain to absolute knowledge. Biological evolution brings us back to very much the same idea, although by quite another approach; and Teilhard de Chardin is drawn into speculations whose fundamentals recall those of Hegelianism.[1] He too foresees a progressive liberation of the spirit. Long before Hegel, Christian doctrine taught that the people of God would only gradually come to maturity, and St. Thomas held that the sanctification of the individual was a step nearer this end— nearer, that is, to a higher form of existence (and this foreshadows Heidegger); but the idea of religious history was little stressed before Newman. Today the whole universe seems involved

[1] Teilhard opposes Hegel on many points; above all, he does not recognize—or barely recognizes—dialectical progression. It is not, in his view, the interplay of contradictions which causes the world to advance. And it goes without saying that the Christian background of his mind puts him at the opposite pole to Hegel's thought.

in history. Einstein makes it impossible for us
to conceive of space as something wholly distinct
from time. If he sets before us a more complete
unity of physical knowledge, in which, for instance, the force of gravity is shown as a curve,
it is by making use of space-time, which brings
time into the context of reality.[1] The theory of
the expanding universe emphasizes the evolution of the cosmos, which explains such physical
laws as the increase of entropy.

In his own explanation of the universe, Teilhard assigns a decisive part to duration—a duration which recalls that of Bergson.[2] Teilhard
goes back to the Aristotelian concept of nature
as something developing, expanding; but to him
it assumes other forms and a wholly different
significance. Heidegger explicitly ponders much

[1] I pass over the problems that this raises. Is it concrete reality that is in question; is there not a certain
juggling with the dynamism of the physical data in
order to obtain a more satisfactory mathematical unification? By seeing time as a dimension and force as a
curve, are we not forgetting their uniqueness? On the
other hand, we are made to realize that it is idle to try
to conceive of reality without the dimension of time,
and we shall in future be less tempted to regard objects
as static. Change is part of their very nature.

There is in any case a universal trend in modern
thought, in physics and philosophy, to bring time into
the very heart of things.

[2] Bergson's is more fully worked out, describing as it
does the original phenomena of the flow of consciousness.

the same idea[1]; in his analysis of man's being, he introduces time (in what he calls "concern") as a defining element. It has been observed that a fairly general characteristic of modern thought is its preoccupation with the *subject*, whether individual or collective, and with its developments. There are many points of difference between the various schools of thought; the analogies between the trends of science and of philosophy are but remote, and we must, above all, be on our guard against misleading identifications. But it may be said that certain themes recur, in various forms, in most branches of enquiry.

And contemporary thought is concerned to know why, at a given stage of its history, it is bound to take stock of itself, in a way that, a stage earlier, would have been almost out of the question. We see, for instance, with Heidegger, that ontological history is bound up with the laws of being. It seems, in any case, as if the growth of the human mind now calls for us to take stock of ourselves in many related fields. And this lends further support to the new ideas —that of development, in particular.

(3) *Universalist aspirations* are everywhere so obvious as to be hardly worth mentioning. Man's adventure is collective—so much so that the spiritual life of each is affected by the destiny

---

[1] The φύσις of the pre-Socratics, taken in the sense of φύεις, to unfold.

of all. If a hermit knows what he is doing, he
sees his life as closely linked with the present
state of the world and the principal changes
ahead of it. From the political and even the
religious point of view, we can see that the real
problem lies in saving populations rather than
individuals—and, finally, in saving the whole
human race. Is this idea exaggerated? Possibly;
and in so difficult a matter we must beware of
making up our minds too quickly. What is certain is that the world is trying to discover its own
social unity—in diversity, but on a common
ground.

And we look to science to be a unifying
element—one of the most important of such
elements. Auguste Comte believed it would
become the speculative bond of a universal
society; he had in mind, too, a science of wider
boundaries—positivist philosophy. We are inclined to smile at his simplicity; yet it cannot be
denied that the world is seeking a common
vision, born of scientific knowledge. "To him
alone (whether we are as yet fully aware of it or
not) the setting up of a universal physics,
chemistry and biology inevitably suggested the
first faint outline of planetary interrelation-
ship."[1]

Thus the current of thought springing from
contemporary science takes in vastly more
than the technical labours of mathematicians,

[1] *A*, 353.

physicists and biologists. Not only has a whole group of "human sciences" won recognition—such sciences as the various branches of experimental psychology, anthropology, sociology, political economy and so forth; but the most philosophical form of speculative thought, even when it is not tuned in to science, follows a path that is roughly parallel. We find a certain family likeness in all contemporary thought.[1] Wherever we turn, a new horizon opens. Teilhard de Chardin quotes Henri Breuil's saying: "We have only just cast off the last moorings which held us to the Neolithic age."[2]

A palaeontologist, provided he has a wide enough outlook, is perhaps of all men the best fitted to follow a trajectory in which modern intuitions appear, link up and develop—intuitions based, always, on facts. He has before him the history of the world in its entirety; he studies the emergence of successive waves of phenomena, right up to the phenomenon of man; on all alike he turns the same gaze, as though he saw them from within. There is in Père Teilhard de Chardin a sort of tenderness for the cosmos—and for man, and all other forms of life; an intuitive familiarity with the whole universe. He is determined to stay within the

[1] And indeed modern thought elaborates the idea of a *global form* (*Gestalt*) applicable to a type of behaviour, or a thought.

[2] *P*, 214.

boundaries of science, never straying beyond the level of phenomena, but merely observing their chief data and drawing ultimate conclusions from them. It will be worth our while to shed all our preconceived opinions and listen attentively to what he has to tell us. We shall find ourselves wondering whether he does not, after all, step outside the field of science; whether his conclusions are wholly convincing; whether one is right to expect so much from scientific thought. But on all this, let us not make up our minds beforehand.

The aim of this book is not to applaud Teilhard de Chardin's line of reasoning—and still less to find fault with it—but to indicate the chief problems that it raises, and begin, at least, to ponder them. I shall argue not for the sake of arguing, but in an attempt to discover what certainties (or near-certainties) come to light from among more debatable interpretations. Such discrimination—and very sensitive it has to be— is called for throughout Teilhard's works. There are now grounds for hoping, both that we may achieve objective knowledge, and that we may find a plan of concerted action; but for this we need solid facts; and when the solid and the uncertain are intermingled, we must do what we can to find an impregnable foundation.

PART 1

COSMOLOGY

2

THE IMAGE OF THE UNIVERSE

IT is as well to keep Père Teilhard de Chardin's central idea before one's eyes right from the start. All subsequent developments in the cosmological order are closely connected with it, and it is the subject of the more philosophical comments that we shall come to later. We shall understand the whole thing better if we do not lose sight of the intuition underlying it all—an intuition which is put into words in the following passage:

> Studied at sufficient depth (millions of years), life is on the move: and not only is it on the move, but it is going forward in a given direction, and we are able to follow, quite clearly, the process or mechanism of its advance.
>
> ... from the lower to the higher, in all forms known to us (however involved the ramifications may be), there is a perfectly discernible trend of zoological types leading to animals of a more elaborate and concentrated nervous system.
>
> ... What does all this mean if not that,

throughout the ages, a rising tide of consciousness is at work—a slow ascent, made visible to
us by the growth of nervous systems?

. . . the march of time can (and should) be
measured by a progressive concentration of
matter, which becomes haloed with an increasingly radiant light of freedom and consciousness. Consciousness on earth down the
ages has never ceased to grow as a direct consequence of the more advanced organization of
increasingly complex elements, made up of
chemical and living energies.[1]

Evolution begins with the combination of
elementary particles (neutrons, electrons) to
form an atomic structure.

Above are the molecules, formed by groups
of atoms. These molecules, in compounds of
carbon, may become enormous. In albumi-
noids (or proteins) there may be thousands of
assembled atoms; the molecular weight is
68,000 in the haemoglobin of the blood.

Higher yet are the mysterious viruses,
strange bodies which cause various illnesses in
animals and plants, and of which we cannot
yet say whether they represent monstrous
chemical molecules or infra-bacteria that are
already alive. Their molecular weight is of
several million!

[1] "L'Avenir de l'homme, vues d'un paléontologiste",
in Cité nouvelle, 10 June 1941.

If we go higher still, we come to the first cells; I do not know whether anyone has yet tried to determine their atomic content (which must run into billions), but they are certainly built up from proteins.

And, finally, we reach the world of higher living beings, each one made up of a group of cells; here, in the very simple instance of the water-bean, it has been found possible to estimate a content of 4×10^{20} atoms! [1]

Living forms share in the general trend towards more advanced organization and increasing psychic powers, as though some law of gravity (or, rather, its opposite—a law pulling them upwards) were continually drawing them in the same direction. It is this general fact that Teilhard never tires of stressing throughout his works. His whole thought revolves round this axis of evolutionary "gravity".

Taken in its broadest sense, the idea expresses an undeniable truth. But we must be careful to understand it aright, or we may draw the wrong conclusions from it. For it does contain a problem. [2] It is a problem inherent in nature, teasing and fascinating: a problem, too, no doubt, in Père Teilhard de Chardin's own train of

[1] "Vie et planète", in *Études*, May 1946.
[2] This, despite the assurance of certain sentences: "We can trace quite clearly the process or mechanism of this progression." (*Cité nouvelle*, 10 June 1941.)

thought, for one can never be sure, on rereading
him, whether one has seized his exact meaning.
It seems only fair to make a serious effort to see
it aright, and to go through all the principal
points of the question, one by one.

A scientist cannot always provide a clinching
demonstration of his concept of the universe.
He comes, through his meditations, to *feel* the
world—in conformity, it need hardly be said,
with physical laws and the data of experience,
but amplifying more or less certain facts by an
intuitive vision. At times—and this seems to be
the case with Teilhard—the intuitive vision
comes very early—in youth or even in child-
hood; later studies only serve to make it more
definite. In this vision of the world there are
some aspects that are classical, demonstrable;
others, more personal, that are put forward as
mere suggestions, although the author himself
set great store by them, even if he could not give
a very definite outline to his thought.

To Teilhard de Chardin, the whole universe
co-operates, in some way or other, in the evolution of living things; and the whole universe is
evolving. Thus it is possible to speak of a cosmogenesis—that is, an act gradually accomplished
by the whole cosmos. The universe is a whole;
it forms a coherent unity; moreover, this unity
is in its earliest stages, and the coherence
becomes more marked as time goes on. The
universe is far more intelligible if we set it

against its own future and see in the present traces of organization the first faint outline of a more perfect unity. To put it briefly, we must learn to understand the *"irreversible coherence of all that exists"*. *"The distribution, succession and solidarity of objects are born from their concrescence in a common genesis.* Time and space are organically joined again so as to weave, together, the stuff of the universe".[1]

Let us first examine this idea of a *Weltstoff*, which sums up several important points.

(1) We must consider *total Matter*, with the whole volume of the universe. "As a kind of gigantic 'atom', it forms in its totality ... the only real indivisible."[2]

We can, of course, discern successive zones or envelopes—atom, molecule, planet, galaxy, cosmos. But, if we only study one of these wholes, we fail to see the totality of the properties of matter. If we concentrate on too small a part, all the resources of which the concrete reality is capable do not come into play, and are not discoverable. If we knew nothing of organized matter—that is to say, the world of life—we could explore physics and chemistry for ever without once suspecting the extraordinary properties that appear when the same elements (atoms, molecules) acquire the precise organization of animal tissue, of a nervous system. And, of course, we are even further from guessing at

[1] *P*, 218.   [2] *P*, 43.

an entire species; furthest of all, from ever dreaming of the zoological totality. Contrary to the idea conveyed in Pascal's famous words on the two infinities, the atom is not a small solar system in which there is a world containing minute particles which can themselves be split in the same way as the atom itself. The structural type, when the scale is changed, is completely different, and what appear to be similarities do so only at first sight, and on a very rough approximation. "These multiple zones of the cosmos envelop without imitating each other in such a way that we cannot pass from one to another by a simple change of coefficients." "The mesh of the universe is the universe itself."[1] It can only be known in its entirety.

(2) "The volume of each of them"—each atom—"is the volume of the universe."[2] For it is integral with all the rest. Needless to say, it has its own dimensions. But it reacts on other physical realities—atoms and assemblages—and is affected by them in turn. Above all, it too is swept along by the same universal process of development.

In the first place, it is subject to the influence of the whole—"The sphere above the centres and enveloping them".[3] On this point, Teilhard's argument is neither very fully worked out nor very exact; as he himself says, he is more

[1] *P*, 45.
[2] *P*, 45.
[3] *V*, 137, 138.

of a naturalist than a physicist, and it is impossible for a man to be a specialist in every field. Yet he seems to regard the universe as a whole, immanent in each of its points; a collectivity of laws, forces, properties is present wherever there is a grain of matter; yet the most important of these properties belong to the whole as a whole. Some of them—or others—appear at the level of smaller totalities—the biosphere, or even a phylum, or even an organism.

Alongside the properties resulting from the collective interplay of parts, there must be, in every organized whole, certain other properties, whether ponderable or otherwise; the prerogative of the whole as such, and which the analyses, or the sum total, of the elementary forces, are never sufficient to account for.[1]

From the point of view of the biologist, the universe appears as a power capable, when certain conditions are fulfilled, of gradually raising up life, and leading it towards higher forms. The phenomena of life and consciousness "may very well be nothing but properties peculiar to a form of matter that has reached a very high degree of arrangement and centralization".[2] "Life is always under pressure everywhere."[3] The cosmos has means of first setting in motion

[1] *V*, 137, 138. [2] *P*, 302.
[3] *P*, 302.

and then directing a process which leads to ever richer and more complex arrangements.

We see at once the vast problems that such an idea entails. Can the same cosmic force direct the formation of large molecules, the modification of an animal phylum, and the destiny of the human race? Ought not the dynamic unity of the universe to be analysed in distinct categories? What, finally, *is* the universe, that it should show such powers of organizing and perfecting life? When we are dealing with human consciousness, do we still observe properties of a *Weltstoff*? We shall return to these questions, and gradually come to see more precisely just how they arise and how we are to set about answering them. They are already implied in the very first statement to be brought into prominence here —the statement that the universe is gradually leading portions of matter towards the realization of a thinking zone (noösphere). If, as Teilhard thinks, the human adventure prolongs evolution, the forces which explain evolutionary "gravity" control also the destiny of the spirit. We shall have to look well into the question of the relationship between the human spirit and the stuff of the universe.

(3) The most primitive form under which we perceive the universe is energy.[1] Matter itself can be transformed into physically measurable energy. But Teilhard gives the word "energy"

[1] *P*, 42.

an extremely wide and somewhat ill-defined meaning, which includes the phenomena of consciousness. It may be taken as the "capacity for action".

We find it easy today to understand that the fundamental material datum should be a capacity for action and movement. We know very well that everything is changing, that forces—electrical, magnetic, chemical and so on—are ceaselessly at work, and that, if there is a development of the universe, it is natural enough that the very nature of cosmic reality should be related to energy. But Teilhard, following Bergson and Le Roy, has come to have less everyday views. To him, reality is a gestation, a call, a capacity for adventure, rather than a result that has already been achieved; inner energy or the "within" of things is, in the last analysis, of a psychic nature, or can at least be compared with a faint foreshadowing of psychism. There is, in the stuff of the universe, something like a power of invention, a confused searching which gradually gropes its way towards the phenomena of consciousness. This, as we shall see, is one of the most ticklish points in Père Teilhard's reasoning. We shall, of course, go into this thesis separately and in more detail.

(4) It seems but fitting that we should especially consider that unity which best lends itself to examination: the earth. There, more than anywhere, shall we find described the properties

of the *Weltstoff*: above all, we shall study life
on earth, seen as making up a specific whole.
And the properties in that whole are already
visible, to quite a striking extent, in less vast
wholes—although they have to be of a certain
size. When any fairly large population of animals is geographically cut off, it becomes differentiated by evolution and splits up into
certain functional groups—always the same:
runners, climbers, swimmers, herbivores, carnivores, insectivores. "Do we not see in these facts
an autonomous power of organization, of
differentiation, which is not localized in individuals but diffused in a fairly large proportion
of animate matter?"[1] Any moderately large fragment of life tends to "reproduce the general
design of the tree from which it was cut." These
facts reveal, quite unmistakably, one property
of the stuff of the universe—a power of organization, bringing into being predetermined structures. This conclusion, at which Teilhard stops
short, ought not to make us slacken in our quest
for the mechanisms at work; even though we
may not as yet see the full explanation, we shall
perhaps hit on part of it. It may possibly be
something relatively simple, with no particular
mystery about it. The natural background holds
out a certain number of possibilities which the
animals in question gradually discover through

[1] *V*, 138.

methods of trial and error.[1] Moreover, the various animals collected in the same region form a group (biocoenosis) which tends to cohere, and which ends by finding a way of life, a co-ordinated life in which all functions are fulfilled, whether of herbivores, carnivores, scavengers, parasites or any others.[2]

The scientist first suspects that such links exist, and then goes on to prove that they do. Biological evolution seems to be connected with the maturation of the planet Earth—with, for instance, some chemical change, such as the progressive granitization of the continents. Certain geological phenomena (folding, transport, the distribution of continents) can probably only be understood if seen in conjunction with the evolution of the Earth-unity.[3] It is, indeed, likely

[1] See, on p. 25, *n.*, Simpson's explanation of how, from horses that ate leaves, there came into being a group of horses that grazed.

Many converging arguments seem to show that nature offers but few possible answers to any given need. Thus, three marine vertebrates belonging to very different groups discovered similar forms which adapted them to swift swimming: *Ichthyosaurus* (a fossilized reptile); the shark (a Selachian fish), and the dolphin (a Cetacean mammal). Cf. Cuénot, *L'Évolution biologique*, Masson, 1951, p. 84. There are other examples on pp. 83–8.

[2] See Cuénot's study of the balance of fauna, in *Évolution biologique*, especially pp. 349 ff.

[3] *V*, 152, 153. See the suggestions put forward in a letter to H. Termier, *V*, 68, 69.

enough that even biological evolution should
be related to the whole history of the cosmos;
that it should be studied "from an increasingly
cosmic point of view", in relation to the "evolution of the fundamental mass of the universe".[1]
We must bear in mind these views of Père
Teilhard de Chardin's, which, with science
where it now stands, can hardly be more definite.
We shall have to come back to them when we
compare Teilhard's concept with that of
François Meyer: the contrast we shall find
between the two types of explanation ought not
to blind us to the fact that much of the idea
underlying them is common to both. Teilhard
de Chardin not only believes in a "force of
gravity" which leads to the growth and succession of phyla, but he is inclined to relate this
general tendency to a cosmic phenomenon which
he regards as its chief cause.

The unity of the universe is that of a whole,
involved in one single process of development,
and achieving, over vast periods of time, one
single construction. We should be under a misapprehension regarding the face of the universe,
and its unity, if we failed to realize that this
advance was the most important thing about it—
just as we should misunderstand the coherence
of an embryo or a seed if we were unaware that
it grew into a complete organism or a tree.

[1] *V*, 153.

The discovery of time has won such common acceptance today, and Père Teilhard de Chardin has written about it so clearly, that there is no need to go into it here. He does not overlook the difficulties of transformation; it goes without saying that a naturalist would not be respecting the facts were he to imagine a linear evolution in which all the forms he came across lay in the same line of genetic succession. It has been thought (so Teilhard explains) that the modern horse is descended from *Hipparion*: whereas *Hipparion* has more complicated teeth and cannot be its ancestor.[1] Under microscopic analysis, the phyla give the impression of evaporating.[2] The true lineates form a confused network; but we must learn to make out its general design, as we might that of a sheaf of corn or the intricate web of a feather. The phyla are, as it were, directed. And the whole of life shows, through the ages, one all-embracing trend towards greater complexity.

The first naïve misconceptions of transformation, as Teilhard sees it, are now abandoned, and it has become reduced to a necessary principle— a principle which oversteps the merely biological field. Everything is a phylum, everything is in a state of preparation, everything has always pre-existed, in a rudimentary form, from the beginning of the world. The universe is

[1] *V*, 20.   [2] *V*, 387.

continually, unceasingly, being perfected: all that is born today comes out of the past, and its history goes back to the first moments of the universe (if it ever had any first moments). A man's history begins with the virus, the molecule, the formation of the carbon atom, and even further back still. The breath that swells our hearts "set out at the same time as the light from the first stars".[1]

Thus, each element is not only coextensive with the totality of space, in the sense that the total stuff of the universe is at work in it, but it is coextensive with the history of the whole; if we look at its preparations and its prolongations, we see that it is coextensive with the whole of time. To understand it completely, we should have to take in the entire past; moreover, any given element, being part of the present universe, conditions (although often to an infinitesimal extent) the entire future. For what the future will be depends on the whole of what the universe now is. Any portion, any fragment of the universe is part of an immense river; its function, its place, its meaning can only be understood in relation to the whole of the river's course.

The principle invoked by Teilhard comprises two parts or two successive phases:

[1] *P*, 224.

Nothing can appear that has not been prepared from all eternity.

The universe is always at work perfecting itself.

We shall accept the first of these theses on the basis of a methodological principle. Science, having gradually come to see what its line of enquiry is, and what mental attitude is therefore called for, now realizes that its specific type of explanation demands a history. This means that if, in some extraordinary way, some object turns up that is outside the line of a continuous succession of phenomena, science can make nothing of it.[1] In a case such as this, a scientist must do all he can to get beyond appearances and discover the unchanging process hidden in what looks like discontinuity. He has made up his mind, once for all, to act in this manner, and he is right, even in the case of his trying to work out a theory of hyperphysics. As for saying that it is impossible to perceive "empirically any entity ... otherwise than as engaged in the time-space

---

[1] This might be the case with certain miracles. I am not saying that any miracles in fact occur; I merely reserve the question. To exclude *a priori* the possibility of any such phenomena would be to adopt an unscientific attitude. No principle, methodological or otherwise, should be abused or have extravagant claims made for it.

series"—that would be rather too daring an assertion.[1]

The second thesis is purely experimental. The universe, at least since the time of the earth's formation, has been, and is, slowly achieving perfection, for life is ascending—acquiring, that is to say, new powers. The whole of the universe has, then, locally, advanced.[2] Life is a tree which has grown, and before there was life the preparations for it had already assumed the aspect of growth, through successive groupings. The *rise of complexity* is a phenomenon that cannot be denied.

It is a phenomenon affecting only a fairly small part of the totality of matter; the universe

---

[1] *P*, 140, *n*. Cf. *V*, 182.
Let us take the appearance of some sudden phenomenon—say, the raising of Lazarus: it would be perceptible to our experience.

Henri Breuil (quoted in *V*, 350) makes what seems to me an excellent comment: "The principle of evolution is none other than scientific method itself, applied to all realities, throughout nature, developing in time. It is the only means at our disposal by which we may try to follow the law of their development and succession, whatever their ontological substratum may be. Without it, we could only compile a descriptive catalogue of things, without attempting to understand them."

[2] If life already existed on other planets, it must have been built up there gradually, and the conclusion is the same.

as a whole is, on the contrary, undergoing a process of dispersal, shown physically in the increase of entropy. The cosmos is on the way to becoming a confused, flattened-out jumble. Palaces fall into ruins, mountains crumble away; the levelling-down is going on everywhere. Life, on the other hand, builds up, differentiates, organizes. The reconciliation of these two opposed principles does not raise any great problem; life is no more an exception to the law of increasing entropy than is a bird's flight to the law of gravity. Life is a restricted cross-current, drawing its force from the main, the entropic, current; or, to change the metaphor, "a weight that goes up, because of the heavier weight that comes down".[1]

The great problem that now faces us is to find a correct description for the world-wide growth of life: "A constantly rising tide below the rhythmic tides of the ages."[2] We must look carefully at the nature of this tide and, if we can, see what causes it. Père Teilhard insists that he is trying to *see*, not to *explain*, but in fact every scientist is on the lookout for an explanation; and in this matter it is fairly obvious that to see and to explain tend to go hand-in-hand. The task of seeing is very much harder than one might think. One always interprets—never more so than when one describes evolution as a rise

[1] *V*, 209.   [2] *P*, 101.

of consciousness. Evolution *may* be just a collection of modifications, produced by chance and
pushed all ways at once; if this is so, consciousness is simply one phenomenon among many.
If evolutionary progress is due mainly to selection, nature is advancing in a systematic manner
towards its highest point of vital power, and
consciousness is only a useful process leading to
this result. Or again we may think of the cosmos
as building up increasingly asymmetrical and
improbable structures—in which case evolution
is aiming at the unlikely combination, and not
directly at consciousness. The two things are
only roughly equivalent. And the choice between
the various descriptions amounts to a choice
between the possible causes, or depends on the
degree of importance that we ascribe to any one
of them—to natural selection, the law of improbability in conjunction with the expansion of
the universe (Meyer's theory), the action of
psychism and what led up to it—or any other.
If a new explanation turns up tomorrow, it will
no doubt serve to modify our present view of the
trend of evolutionary progress. On such knowledge as we now possess (and leaving Meyer's
theory out of it), the dominant factor, as Teilhard admits, does not appear to be constant
throughout evolution. Are we, then, justified in
speaking of one single ascent to complexity-
consciousness? We must look into this further:
it is a question that calls for distinctions.

THE WITHIN OF THINGS

E VOLUTION culminates, with man, in a conscious being; and there is already some "psychism" in animals. Reflecting on this fact, Teilhard comes to the conclusion that all preceding stages, even the earliest molecular arrangements, contained psychism—rudimentary, perhaps, but real. A molecule of silica does not think like a man or feel like an animal; of this Teilhard is very well aware. But he holds that there could not be any thought in the human species unless there had been some preparation for it, some first foreshadowing of consciousness, in even the most primitive corpuscles. It is the application of the principle which claims that there is an unbroken history stretching from the hydrogen atom to the higher manifestations of life. Every element—and the phenomenon of psychism is no exception—is coextensive with time; we should see it as a line, not a point, and the line begins with elementary groupings—the molecule, or even the atom. "If there were no internal propensity to unite, even at a prodigiously rudimentary level—indeed in

2*

the molecule itself—it would be physically impossible for love to appear higher up, with us, in 'hominized' form."[1]

We may at once dismiss a suggestion that might occur to some: Teilhard's argument does not imply the idea that spirit is in a line of ontological continuity with matter. It is possible that a special divine act of creation was necessary for the human soul to be what it is; as to that, the scientist, as scientist, can know nothing, and we are now thinking on the scientific level—the level of phenomena. The spirit, in order to function, makes use of the nervous system and various other processes belonging to animal nature; and although—perhaps on account of its own spiritual character—it puts them on a higher level, it accepts their method of functioning.[2] Psychism belongs on the level of phenomena—i.e., of that which appears (and psychic data are, precisely, the manifestations of our soul; whatever the nature of the soul may be, they are *that* within it which appears to us. They represent the entry of our soul into the field of our experience). The continuity of phenomena between animal and man can hardly be questioned. In any case, the existence of animal

[1] *P*, 264.
[2] Thomist teaching leads to similar conclusions. The soul informs the body; there are many today who forget what this implies.

psychism would be quite enough to persuade Teilhard that there *is* a "within" of things.

We have admitted what may be called the phyletic principle: "Nothing appears that has not been eternally in preparation." I think it is valid as a factor in defining the method of the sciences.[1] Let us see what can be deduced from it here.

We know today that a mass is modified by great speed, whereas, at ordinary speeds, masses appear constant; but even at fairly low speeds there is already a modification, albeit imperceptible. If one body is radioactive, it means that all bodies radiate to some extent.[2] If the complex combination of an animal organism leads up to an interior phenomenon—sensation—then every arrangement involves some inward factor.

Some inward factor—yes. But not perception or consciousness.

On the one hand we are logically forced to assume the existence in rudimentary form (in a microscopic, i.e. an indefinitely diffuse,

[1] It may be compared with what Newman, in the *Essay on Development,* calls the criterion of *anticipation.* A true development reveals what was, in fact, present from the beginning; that which may originally have passed unnoticed becomes apparent when we see the unfolding, the expansion, that takes place in it with its growth.

[2] *P,* 55.

state) of some sort of psyche in every corpuscle
... just as the physicist assumes and can calcu-
late those changes of mass (utterly imperceptible to direct observation) occasioned by
slow movement.[1]

There is, however, a great difference between
the two cases—changes of mass, and psychic
activity. For a change of mass, throughout the
whole gamut of possible speeds, is always of the
same nature, although the numerical values are
different: vegetable life—and, even more, pre-
life—is not of the same nature as animal life, or
human. We cannot compare the psychism of a
flower with that of a man, as we can compare
a small variation of mass with a larger. For this
reason the example is slightly misleading (the
words "just as" go too far).

Since there is consciousness in man, it must
have been prepared from all eternity. Prepared;
but not, perhaps, prefigured. If we apply the
"phyletic principle", we must do so with some
precision. That which precedes psychism and
makes it possible for it one day to exist, is not,
perhaps, itself psychism. A molecule of carbonate
of lime, or even of protein, has no nervous
system, no circulatory system, nor even a first
indication of either; why, then, should it have
any first indication of consciousness? To speak
of elements of consciousness as an "inner face"

[1] P, 301–2.

of the " 'material' external face"[1] seems, then, exaggerated; in any case, it is by no means an inevitable deduction from the principle that was our starting-point. A new postulate has slipped in unobserved. It can be stated thus: In living series, relative homogeneity subsists from beginning to end. But Teilhard does at one stage point out the changes of state that take place in the course of a phyletic series, although from what he says elsewhere one might think he had forgotten his own words. An extremely good comparison, of which he is the author, here turns against him; at a given moment water that is being heated begins to boil; but tepid water does not boil. Quite a small increase of heat, when the right moment has come, causes a new and wholly different phenomenon. "There is evidence for the appearance of consciousness in man ... therefore, half-seen in this one flash of light, it has a cosmic extension, and as such is surrounded by an aura of indefinite spatial and temporal extensions."[2] Spatial and temporal antecedents, undoubtedly; but not a cosmic extension. One might as well say that water boils at any temperature.

It is a pity, too, that Teilhard speaks of universal *consciousness* (even though by "consciousness" he means "perception"). Aristotle's use

[1] *P*, 58. The word "consciousness", as Teilhard uses it, is equivalent to "perception", p. 57, *n*. 1.

[2] *P*, 56.

of words was far more precise: he noted degrees of *immanence*, from the vegetable kingdom right up to the realm of spirit.[1] It is only the higher degree of immanence that is consciousness.

If all this were a mere dispute over words, I should have left it alone. But we can here detect the first signs of yielding to a very dangerous temptation—the temptation to overemphasize the element of psychism in nature. We shall see later how this tendency reappears and develops.

It is all the more unfortunate, in that the line of thought suggested by Teilhard seems, on the whole, convincing and profound. The exaggerations affect that very important part of truth that underlies these considerations. Teilhard rediscovers on his own account certain far-reaching intuitions of Aristotle's: I think he is right in seeing an "inner face" in things.

Teilhard in fact distinguishes two kinds of energy:

(1) Tangential or external energy—the energy that concerns physicists—which governs the

---

[1] In contradistinction to transitive operations, immanent operations are those wherein the subject operating benefits by the result. When a hammer strikes a nail, it is the nail that is driven in. When a geometrician demonstrates a theorem, it is his own mind that is enriched. Immanence, very obvious in the case of human intelligence, also exists *analogically* on lower levels, and is, in Aristotle's opinion, the distinguishing mark of all living things.

physical and chemical relations of the elements to each other; it obeys Carnot's second law (the increase of entropy, the running-down of the universe).

(2) Radial or internal energy, which is given two definitions:

> (a) It draws every group forwards, in the direction taken by evolution—that is to say, "towards ever greater complexity and centricity".[1]
>
> (b) (The more usual definition): Psychic energy, known as radial energy (in man, spiritual energy); the energy that sets up a current between one consciousness and another, and shows itself in various psychological phenomena.[2]

These two definitions do not amount to the same thing. They are fundamentally distinct, with all the distinction inherent in the fact that the energy behind evolution is not of a psychic order. That psychism is an *effect* of evolution, I do not deny; to say that it is the *cause* is to make a completely different claim for it, and one that, by and large, I do not hold to be true. At least the question is raised and should be borne in mind. We shall stick to the second definition, which gives the name of radial

[1] *P*, 65.   [2] *A*, 363.

energy to the sources of psychic operations, or to their first foreshadowings.

In every grouping, and probably in every being in nature, there is radial energy. There is an inner thrust, of which physically measurable acts are another "face".

Aristotle had already expressed what is fundamentally the same idea.[1] It is quite easy to grasp. It is by means of "tangential" energies that a knife cuts, an acid dissolves a metal, or a motor revolves. But when a man thinks or loves, or even when a bud swells or unfolds, these changes are to be ascribed principally to a phenomenon of another order; there are inner sources of action behind them.

And, needless to say, acid does not dissolve a metal without itself undergoing a profound change; underlying all acts of the tangential or exterior type, there is probably an act of the radial or interior type. If the latter did not exist, nothing would happen. We are methodologically forced to take due note of the measurable variations of sizes; the definition of such measurable sizes is the beginning of physics. But a scientist need not shut his eyes to the fact that there is, in physical reality, something resembling sap.

[1] Aristotle distinguishes between *nature* and *power*: nature—the capacity for change (or rest) in oneself; power—the ability to produce change (or rest) in another. The word "power" has nothing in common with the concept of potency as opposed to act.

The acts that are its direct consequence are at times disconcerting, for they cannot be measured, whereas in the case of "tangential" acts we can apply that accurate and exact procedure in which the whole honesty of science lies. But a hyperphysics, which sets out to attain the fullest possible understanding of the reality which science is investigating, has much to gain by recognizing those interior aspects which make life the unique thing it is; science itself (even using the word "science" in its strictest sense) profits in the long run, provided that the mind remains sufficiently disciplined, which is possible, even here.

Aristotle's, or Teilhard's, notion of immanence does not take the place of a scientific explanation. It would be a serious mistake to think that one can scamp the hard work that still lies ahead, by juggling with a word that does not give us the final solution. The cohesion that unites the elements of an atom or a molecule is not love; it can, later, be connected with psychic phenomena, as the first step in a long series; this calls for caution (and here Teilhard is not sufficiently on his guard), for the last links in the chain bear little resemblance to the first. But we must be very exact as to the mechanism of living phenomena—growth, nutrition, perception, etc.—and also the rise of the species. When science has found the correct solution to these problems, immanence will seem to melt away in physical laws, in material procedures. And this is just what we must expect. We must not imagine that there is some kindly genie, or some mysterious extra-physical being, existing as one cause among many, made up from them, or taking their place. But the result of these processes, which science will soon be analysing, is a whole made up of immanent acts; we are free to ponder the sources that such acts suggest. Underlying all the calculations, the combinations, the registrable phenomena, there is a natural thrust, which becomes perceptible precisely *through* that which is measurable.

It is a mistake, then, to urge against Teilhard that the attention he pays to psychism does not help the advance of science. It helps us to increase our knowledge of things, to recognize intelligible relations (analogies) which affect vast areas of the cosmos. And it does nothing to delay the discovery of the technical explanation.

But when we have said this—when we have admitted the existence of an inner face of things —there is still a great deal that is vague in Teilhard's treatment of the subject. What *is* the precise nature of radial energy, and what relation does this bear to tangential energies? The explanations suggested for these fundamental problems are really very sketchy.[1] Is radial energy superimposed on material factors, endowing them with organization and direction, in the

[1] *P*. 63–6.

manner of Claude Bernard's "vital principle" or
"directive idea"?[1] It would seem so[2]: but is this
the only part it plays in Teilhard's thought? We
find it inventing, driving evolution on towards
consciousness—and all this is by no means clear.
The first thing that should have been done—
and was not—was carefully to delimit the
functions of radial energy. Teilhard does not

[1] Claude Bernard strongly opposed the idea that a
vital force could be made up of material factors. But
he admitted the existence of a vital principle, and
tried to define its connection with physical principles.
Observation shows us an organic plan, but not an
active *intervention* on the part of a vital principle.
The only *vital force* we can admit would be a kind of
legislative force—legislative, but in no sense executive.
To sum up our views, it might be said metaphorically
that *vital force directs phenomena which it does not
produce; physical agents produce phenomena which
they do not direct.* (*Leçons sur les phénomènes de la
vie communs aux animaux et aux végétaux*, p. 51.)
Claude Bernard's "vital principle" is often compared
with Aristotle's "form" or "soul" (cf. Sertillanges, *La
Philosophie de Claude Bernard*, Aubier, ch. 4). Now,
Teilhard's "radial energy" seems to me to bear quite a
strong resemblance to Aristotle's "nature" (yet is it
quite that?). If it is so, Teilhard's "radial energy" is
not the same thing as Claude Bernard's "vital force".
For, to Aristotle, if form is nature, then even matter
is nature, too, although to a lesser degree. Substantial
form and nature do not coincide. We see from this
both how careful we must be to avoid all hasty comparisons, and how difficult it is, in this context, to know
exactly what is being said.
[2] *V*, 134-5.

altogether steer clear of contradictions in what he says of the extension of psychism and the almost psychic nature of matter, the part played by the inventive force which he believes in, its relation to physical factors, and, finally, the share that this force has had in evolutionary progress.

Consciousness or psychism as another aspect of complexity: this is one of the architraves of Teilhard's cosmology. And the thesis seems incontestable, as long as it is made quite clear what kind of complexity is here in question. We must, in fact, distinguish "among the innumerable complications undergone by organic matter in ebullience . . . those which are merely superficial diversifications and those (if any) which would represent a renewal and re-grouping of the stuff of the universe".[1] As soon as nervous systems appear on the tree of life, we recognise a type of complexity which goes with characteristic attributes—those of psychism. Before this stage, it is less obvious.

If we are to say that there is in fact a universal correspondence between complexity and consciousness (psychism), we must confine the word "complexity" to arrangements of certain types. True complexity is not to be defined by the number and variety of the elements forming the whole; it must also have an organization, or a centre, or an interiority, brought about by

[1] P_{ν} 143.

multiple relations between the elements.[1] Thus a planet is not complex, in the only sense that concerns biology; it is not sufficiently interconnected, and is almost totally lacking in organization. In one of the higher mammals, on the other hand, the interaction of sensations and of the motor regulating the brain, shows very many interconnections and a closely-knit organization.

These remarks, which Teilhard develops more fully, are certainly true. One must, however, add one observation, in an attempt to define exactly what kind of centration or interiority an arrangement must have, if perception or invention is to go with it.

An electronic machine is extremely complex; its parts are interrelated in a very high degree; but nevertheless it possesses no psychism. It carries out difficult operations; but although the result is within itself, it is not aware of them. It is incapable of doing what seems to us the simplest thing of all; it cannot know what it has written; it cannot read the result. Moreover, as Léon Brillouin has pointed out, there is an enormous difference between its workings and the powers of the human mind; the mathematical machine never adds to its information. It invents nothing. It translates into another form the facts that it has been made to register. It does not imagine. If it is made to work backwards, it

[1] G, 17, V, 313.

gets back to exactly the same data from which it started. Nowhere, in any compartment of the machine, can one find invention, imagination, reflection, creative thought, or initiative.[1]

This example shows us that complexity does not automatically become psychism through the mere presence of interconnections. For that to happen, there has to be the very special type of arrangement that constitutes life. There is, moreover, a certain resemblance between the mechanism of a calculating machine and the human brain; the interplay of the connections, as has often been pointed out, is much the same in both. Life, then, contains, over and above that resemblance, one decisive factor which is lacking to the machine. What factor? We shall not solve the riddle, but it had to be pointed out in passing. Life, doubtless, is the realization of another type of organization; so that the likeness to mechanism, which suggests the comparison with the calculating machine, is incomplete. It holds good on the level of certain structures, but leaves room for what are no doubt profound differences, as we see if we study more closely the very special organization brought into being by nature. An electronic brain is more complicated than are many animals; but it is not alive. In defining complexity as multiplicity of inter-

[1] Cf. Brillouin, "La Vie, la pensée et la physico-chimie", in Les Cahiers de la pléïade, 13, Autumn 1951–Spring 1952.

relations we have not yet put our finger on the specific reality which causes the appearance of life and psychism. This calls for interrelations of a somewhat special kind.

These remarks are not intended as an attack on Teilhard's theories, for they do not affect his argument as a whole; but the main question is still left open. We admit that, all along the tree of life, or at least on that twig of it which buds forth in man, there is an "increase of the synthetic state of matter [which] involves, we said, an increase of consciousness for the milieu synthesized".[1] None the less, the law linking complexity with psychism only holds good for those types of complexity called into being by life.

[1] *P*, 89.

4

THE SPRING OF LIFE

ÈRE TEILHARD de Chardin's main preoccupation was to trace, and to understand, the progress of evolution. How does it help us to gain a better understanding of that worldwide fact—the rise of species—if we consider the "inner face" of things? Will evolutionary "gravity" thereby become any more intelligible to us? The "within" advances throughout the centuries, for more highly developed psychisms come into being; the universe is contracting, that is to say, becoming concentrated, in living things, and its properties are intensifying. Is it possible to describe evolution, taken as a whole, as an upsurge of complexity-consciousness? To what extent, and by what process, can the force known as radial (or internal) energy urge living forms in the direction in which we see them tending? These questions call for careful enquiry.

The evolution of life certainly involves an ascent towards complexity and consciousness— the evolution of that form of life, at any rate, which leads to the human species. There is, then, in fact, a "law of complexity-consciousness"—in other words, a simultaneous progress of both aspects; but it has to be interpreted aright. And concern to find this right interpretation will not be out of place, especially when we are called upon, by reason of this law, to forecast the future.

As Teilhard sees it, the flux of life (he even speaks of cosmogenesis) is "only definable in accretions of consciousness".[1] The formula is exaggerated; there are other ways of defining the advance of evolution, and it is not certain that this definition gives the truest picture of the facts. According to Meyer, the whole procedure can and should be defined as an advance towards the improbable (towards structures the fortuitous realization of which would be very unlikely). The improbable is, of course, complex; and the complex, built up by life, is, in fact, accompanied by psychism. The net result is perhaps the same if the universe is in fact moving systematically towards consciousness; but the way in which this result comes about is of great importance if we want to understand the real direction of the evolutionary drive. Let us now assume that the most powerful factor in evolution is natural selection; in that case, the advantage goes not only to those animals which manage to survive their many dangers, but also to male animals which oust other males when it

[1] P, 220.

comes to mating. On them, the whole future of
the species depends. Evolution, then, is moving,
not towards consciousness, nor towards improbable structures, but towards the highest
degree of vital power at the actual time of
mating, even if the male loses his advantage
later on.[1] In this case, complexity and consciousness are the accidental consequences of a law
whose specific effect is to increase vital power.

We do not know enough about the nature of
evolutionary "gravity" to know whither it is
tending by its direct effect. This being so, can
we speak of an "absolute direction of advance
towards the values of increasing consciousness"?[2]
The absolute direction is not clear enough to be
determined with any certainty.

Is there, indeed, only one direction? As
Rostand sees it, evolutionary phenomena do not
seem to be all tending to one end.

The picture presented to us of life's evolution astounds us by its high talents ... and
disconcerts us by the use to which they are

[1] There is the well-known example of the Irish elk,
whose antlers, while it was young, gave it the advantage
in fights, but later became so over-developed and un-
wieldy as to be a serious, even a disastrous, encum-
brance.
There is some discussion as to how this instance
should be interpreted (cf. Simpson, *Tempo and Mode
in Evolution*, New York, 1944, pp. 171 ff.
[2] *V*, 340.

put. Incoherent, unprovident, wasteful and tumultuous, as heedless of failure as of success; creating at random in every style and direction; prodigal in discarding the new; launching one species against another; creating both harmony and the grotesque; unmindful of what is necessary but meticulous in what is superfluous, and creating impartially that which will survive through the ages, that which will degenerate and that which will continue to progress.[1]

Such "branching-out" (to use Teilhard's word) as this may show a relative singleness of advance if, in addition to the local causes that make for diversity, there is a systematic factor driving in a certain direction. What is this factor? Is it unique, and the same at the beginning and end of evolution? This will long remain an open question, and we must bear in mind the uncertainty that surrounds it.

Teilhard's views are often very wise and cautious:

During the first, immensely long, period of pre-life, chance alone, as far as we can tell, seems to have had a hand in forming the first complexes. Higher up, when we come to pre-human life, there is a wide contested area where, according to some—the

[1] Rostand, *A Biologist's View*, Heinemann, 1956, pp. 25-6.

neo-Darwinians—it is still chance alone, and,
according to others—the neo-Lamarckians—
it is chance, certainly, but chance used and
controlled by a principle of interior self-
organization—which is responsible for weav-
ing the biosphere. Higher up still, once the
threshold of reflection has been crossed, the
psychic power to combine at last appears in
the individual, made possible by their great
numbers—appears as a specific and normal
factor of hominized life.[1]

Whatever the factor at work may be, the result
is a rise towards consciousness. And there, precisely, as we may allow, is the law of the evolutionary drive throughout the ages. We have yet
to establish the exact nature of the mechanisms,
but quite certainly they lead on to more and
more organized groupings. A physical cause
(using the phrase in a very wide sense) unwittingly creates complex structures, trying all
possible directions, losing its way in many blind
alleys, and sometimes bringing off astonishing
feats of equilibrium. Teilhard describes a
"groping" process which is very like this.[2] We
come back to his description of the facts if we
admit that the "absolute direction" of evolution
is the complex as such. For he adds that since
the Without of things always has its Within, the

[1] G, 146.
[2] See especially P, 110.

inevitable accompaniment of complexity is psychism.

Does the law of complexity-consciousness thus arrived at hold good throughout the whole world of nature? It applies, undoubtedly, all along the branch that bears the primates and their fore-runners. Elsewhere it is less apparent; where the nervous system is lacking, we cannot say that evolutionary progress tends unmistakably to-wards perception and invention. We should have some difficulty in tracing the rise of psychism in the vegetable kingdom ... The law of com-plexity-consciousness is attested in the series leading to man; and this is already much.

"It provides a direction; and by its conse-quences *it proves that evolution has a direc-tion*."[1] A direction? To us, certainly. But what meaning has it *for the cosmos*? At this point we come up against a tendency to anthropo-morphism which should be noted at once. In all probability the cosmos has no aim in view, does not "want", even confusedly, to construct a brain. The universe throws forth its actions, in obedience to laws of which it knows nothing, in all directions at once; and it so happens, through sheer physical necessity, that one of the phyla ends up as man—man with his brain. The notion that a divine mind conceived the idea of man and organized a universe which, after many setbacks, succeeded in producing him—all this

[1] *P*, 146.

raises quite another question, and the moment has not yet come for considering it. If it is the universe that we are talking about, we can note the direction of its advance—or several directions. As to what all this implies in the cosmos itself, this is precisely what we are enquiring into, and we must not start by ruling out any hypothesis: but we must ask ourselves what cosmic meaning the word "sense" ("the sense of history", the "sense of evolution") can have. It is equivalent to "direction", or orientation of fact; not to "meaning" or "significance". Or else it implies a "meaning", a "significance", which the universe offers *to our mind*; that should be noted. An epistemological question of major interest lies in distinguishing between those meanings which are unmistakable (given what our mind is and what it cannot fail to be), and subjective interpretations based on imagination or our own gullibility. We are fond of arguing as though we ourselves had been the master minds behind the universe, which we see as a machine carefully made to achieve a certain purpose. Scientific objectivity, it need hardly be said, requires us to deal very sternly with this first temptation.

When we have done so, we shall begin by thinking that the universe is moving in all directions at once; then, that there is, due to factors of which at present we know little, one chosen direction, an evolutionary gravity. This it is that leads, above all, to psychism; which does not mean that we should define it as directly contrived to produce this effect.

The following solution then occurs to us. A natural factor—or several natural factors—leads or lead to the building up of co-ordinated and increasingly complex structures; from among an enormous number of contingencies and attempts in every direction, one tendency continues to appear—a drive towards ever vaster and more effective combinations. The universe, then, is creating increasingly rich, complex arrangements; at least certain types of arrangement—and life pours them forth lavishly enough—have a psychic aspect.

But is this what Teilhard meant? It would seem that he went further. It is consciousness as such which he believed to be the specific effect of cosmogenesis; life, to him, was "a movement of consciousness veiled by morphology".[1]

What would be the prerequisite for such a state of affairs? Simply that the stuff of the universe should be of a psychic nature. If indeed its properties are completely covered by chemico-mathematical analysis—if, for instance, it can be reduced to a collection of particles moving in a field of forces—it may evolve towards the improbable, but it can never tend systematically towards consciousness. On the other hand, if it is already consciousness, or something very like

[1] P, 167–8.

it, it can advance towards an improved form of consciousness.[1] It is possible that psychism is trying (confusedly) to develop along its own axis, and is slowly climbing upwards to higher forms.

Père Teilhard de Chardin was sufficiently cautious not to attribute deliberate thought, or even an instinct comparable with that of animals, to the stuff of the universe outside the realm of living things. He admitted that it was only in the Neolithic period that the "influence of psychical factors began, in man, to outweigh those of the somatic".[2] As far as the greater part of the tree of life—and pre-life, even more—was concerned, he believed in material causes.

But he believed that matter itself is of its nature psychical, in a real though rudimentary sense. We must try to see what he was driving at; his idea is, I think, fundamentally very interesting.

He was reacting against a purely mechanistic conception of the material datum—a conception which is, indeed, common enough. On the one hand, the image-type which to us stands for matter is all too often a stone—motionless, scentless, ponderable, passive. On the other hand,

[1] "Consciousness tending invincibly (like an idea in one's head) to complete itself right to the end, but only able to do so if it can arrange." (G, 36.) Two other hypotheses are put forward, but it is easy to see from Teilhard's works as a whole, where his predilection lies.
[2] P, 207.

some degree of scientific training, especially in the case of people with very little sense of biology, accustoms the mind to purely quantitative considerations; the purely mechanistic outlook imagines a geometrical point endowed with mass, and subject to vector forces. Any such concept of real matter, even with the addition of chemical properties, would be a travesty. We have built up, to meet the requirements of elementary science, an abstract scaffolding in support of numerical data. And, certainly, science is quite right in being everywhere on the lookout for the measurable. But physical matter, real physical matter, has other aspects, which may be roughly described as "qualitative". This is not to say that such aspects are not to be explained by quantitative arrangements, for the organization of matter causes new properties to appear; but we must learn to recognize such properties wherever they occur, and they may well exist even on the level of the inanimate universe.

This, no doubt, is why Teilhard did not hesitate to imagine "an 'innate' (and therefore scientifically inexplicable) preference on the part of the stuff of the universe for higher states of complexity and consciousness".[1] At first impact, the words make one leap out of one's chair: so the universe proceeds by "preferences"! —in conjunction, it is true, with measurable laws . . .

[1] *V*, 369, *n*.

3+

Then we begin to see a glimmer of daylight (although we must still be on our guard). Quite possibly, we should admit the existence of a property of the All which to all intents and purposes is the same thing as a chosen, a favourite direction. This, no doubt, is not scientifically inexplicable; but if we are to make this property intelligible, we shall have to describe the structure of the cosmos, working out the synthesis from the macroscopic as well as the microscopic point of view; for we must bear in mind both the organization of the universe as a whole, and the inmost nature of matter. As we know, Teilhard insisted both that we should consider the whole universe, and that matter is energy. It is this energy, taken at the level of the All, which may be identified with a favourite direction and show a qualitative aspect. When such a synthesis comes to be made, it may well give us quite a new idea of the stuff of the universe. Teilhard felt this need to widen our concept, and expressed it in his own way.

We are considering the stuff of the universe as being below the level of living things. If we look at the cosmos in its totality, it at present contains man with his thinking mind; but this does not entitle us to say that the stuff of the universe can think (I am sure that Père Teilhard never made such a howler), for there is no thought apart from individual human beings. To speak of the All of the universe, without being more explicit, might well be misleading. One aspect of the question concerns the stuff of the universe as a cause, evolutionary gravity: the real datum capable of determining the general trend of life. That datum, which was already at work before the appearance of the virus, has neither the thought of man nor the instinct of the animal. Nor can it be reduced to a piece of mechanism; there is in it a kind of sap or onrush—what Aristotle called "nature". If we were able to be more exact, we should no doubt have to arrive at a wholly new concept, as different from a "preference" or an invention of the instinct as from some lifeless geometrical material.

I think we owe Teilhard a debt for having put forward an almost biological conception of matter and the cosmos. Unfortunately he goes, I think, too far. He tends to identify the fundamental impetus of cosmogenesis with psychism properly so-called, and attributes too much importance to this characteristic. To say that the world is based on freedom and ingenuity[1] is to speak the language of poetry—especially when what is in question is the most elementary form of life, or pre-life.

According to Teilhard, an animal is carnivorous because, "following its line of descent, it receives, develops and hands on the 'soul of a

[1] *P*, 110.

carnivore' "[1]; the form of its teeth is the result. But if this is the way evolution takes place, we must allow that acquired characteristics are transmitted; we can understand that the animals of a given group develop the psychism of carnivores, but do they hand it on in a developed state?[2] It may very well be true that the anti-Lamarckism so prevalent in the twentieth century has been too sweeping[3]: we shall perhaps have to come back to the view that what is acquired can *to some extent* be transmitted; but it is extremely doubtful whether this transmissibility is the *principal* explanation of evolution.

[1] *P*, 150. Cf. *V*, 134, *V*, 282–3.
[2] Cf. *A*, 333.
[3] Lamarckism tries to find inner explanations for evolution—explanations in which the activity of living things plays a large part (whereas Darwinian selection points to external causes). To Lamarck, it is the function which shapes and develops the organ—a mole's eyes become atrophied because it lives in the dark; a giraffe's neck grows longer because he is always trying to reach leaves far above him—and so on. The organism is transformed by its efforts to adapt itself to its surroundings; and successive generations, by multiplying the examples, render visible modifications that would pass unnoticed if only a single life-span were under observation. But the improvements which the individual acquires during its lifetime have to be passed on to its descendants. Now, it is generally thought that acquired characteristics cannot be transmitted. We should not rule out the possibility that so definite an assertion requires some qualification, and that Lamarckism is entitled to its niche, although perhaps a small one.

It probably does no more than introduce slight modifications.

As to the part played by invention in the development of life, we read what is probably a perfect description: "We could never give a *complete* explanation of the appearance and setting of the wing, the fin, or even the eye or brain, without *to some extent* introducing the faculties and psychical processes brought into play by these innovators."[1] Teilhard adds: "There is nothing *a priori* to prove that, on a level below man, the same factor [exists but] is so weak as to pass unnoticed." And again: "We cannot be sure that this psychism (of the non-reflective type) is not so entirely different from our own in its modalities and functionings as to make any comparisons between the two misleading and futile."

Why should these difficulties be cancelled in other passages by a sort of enthusiastic impetus of spirit? It is hard to see why we have to resort to the "dominating and continual influence of an 'inventive power'—'inventive' here meaning 'psychical'—to explain physically either the constant rise of elements to build up increasingly improbable structures; or, during this ascent, the astounding expansions of spontaneity that we are witnessing."[2] At the birth of a phylum Teilhard sees (instinctive) invention, the awakening of

[1] *V*, 330. [2] *V*, 221.

desire and power.[1] I have already quoted the two
definitions (taken to be interchangeable) of
radial energy; it is at once psychical energy and
the energy that causes the advance of evolution.
Teilhard admits "the spontaneous activity of
individuals"[2] in the genesis of phyla—combined,
it should be added, with the determinism of the
genes. He certainly seems, in many passages, to
be ascribing the chief agency to what is a near-
psychism.

Such an approach goes much further than the
more moderate passages that have seemed to me
the fairest statement of the case. The objections
that it raises will be brought out more fully in
the next chapter, but we may look at a few of
them now. We have already seen how dangerous
it is to exaggerate the psychical (or, better, pre-
psychical) characteristics of matter. But let us
take the case of even the higher animals (man
excepted), in which instinct and perhaps invention are far advanced. In what way can these
psychical powers direct morphological evolution? What they direct above all is the life of
the individual. Interior energy, being the result
of an assemblage, is, in its most clearly seen
effects, linked up with the individual organism.
For, if the vegetable and animal kingdoms are
living assemblages, and have, therefore, their
own interior energy, this energy is but slight,
for the connections are far slacker. In the case

[1] *V*, 135.   [2] *P*, 225.

of an individual organism, the functions of interior energy are fairly obvious; it regulates the animal's behaviour in all the perils and difficulties that face it. We may believe that, when it comes to a whole species, this energy has yet other functions, but it is not easy to say what they are—not easy, especially, to explain how it can bring about an offshoot of the species. Either what we are discussing is individual psychism, or it is psychism of quite another kind:

(a) Individual psychism does indeed play some part in evolution, for it enters into selection; the act of mating pre-supposes at least a minimum of choice in which instinct has some say; moreover, unadapted psychism would incur for the animal the penalty of an earlier death. But such acts seem too trivial to explain the vast phenomena which determine evolution. The future of a species depends above all on its fertility; when it is more fertile than other species it ousts them. Compared with such facts the psychism of individuals carries very little weight. Moreover, any argument in favour of an individual factor comes up against the difficulties raised by the transmission of acquired characteristics.

(b) We can avoid this difficulty by considering the collective psychism of a population of animals. In this case what concern us are the modifications introduced into the psychism of individuals by the influences of their environ-

ment. These influences may at times be lasting
and extend over a great many generations. So
there is, no doubt, a psychic aspect in fertility,
and it may be as well to draw attention to it;
but this psychic aspect has been brought about
by innumerable chances, which do not set out
systematically in search of the highest possible
degree of consciousness . . . That type of psychism
explains the localized orientations of evolution,
but it is not in itself a systematic cause capable
of determining a general trend of life.

(c) Teilhard seems to see in the universe a
growing force of desire and invention (more confused at the start): a force that at first is very
unsure of itself, but that gradually grows in
intensity until it culminates in human psychology. Thenceforth it is no longer enough to
think of relatively small populations among
which collective influences are at work. We must
now consider a psychism of the larger groups;
or of life as a whole; or of the stuff of the
universe. In these conditions, the psychism in
question is too tenuous (if indeed it can be called
psychism at all) to be able to direct a global
variation of living forms.

It is possible to form a different concept of
an *interior* principle of evolutionary progress.
This may not be psychic. In Meyer's hypothesis,
the syntropic flux is an interior principle, just
as is the increase of entropy. And it would be

possible to suggest other interior principles, existing on the same level or on the level of the biosphere. Teilhard has put forward the theory of a connection between vital evolution and (a) the granitization of the continents; or (b) a progressive modification of chemical conditioning; or (c) a supra-individual and unitary maturation of the protoplasm; or (d) some phenomenon affecting the earth-unity.[1] These ideas are no doubt worth looking into. But Teilhard introduces an entirely different principle when he tries to explain evolution by psychism.[2] It is true that the factors he mentions (progressive chemical modification, etc.) have a psychical effect; but they have also, and primarily, somatic effects, which may well be more decisive.

Teilhard thinks, and certainly rightly, that chance does not explain everything; its effects are reduced by a systematic cause, or systematic causes, that may be called an anti-chance. But I feel that Teilhard passes too quickly from this general idea of the anti-chance to that of a Lamarckian and even psychic factor.[3] Many other concepts are possible.[4] In Meyer's theory

[1] *V*, 68, 152, 153.

[2] Especially when he claims that acquired psychical characteristics can be transmitted. (*A*, 333.)

[3] Cf. *P*, 149 *n*.

[4] It should be noted that selection itself is an anti-chance (but an external factor). We reject, of course, the identification of anti-chance with God. (Lecomte du Noüy.) Anti-chances are natural factors.

3*

(even if it does not hold water) we come on an anti-chance factor of another type, more intelligible to scientific thought. It is of course permissible to believe in the part played by some near-psychism; but its usefulness in the evolutionary scheme, and the mechanism by which it works, need to be clarified in discussion far more than they have been.

Teilhard's readers are apt to flag under the torrent of grandiose phrases whose meaning is somewhat uncertain. Bergson's *élan vital*, criticized as it sometimes was, now seems to have been replaced by a "wind of consciousness" or a "cosmic preference", which satisfies the mind no better. One distrusts the "ultimately psychic nature of evolution".[1]

The rise of the cosmos towards consciousness is a hypothesis, and Teilhard knows it; yet he often speaks with far too much assurance. Any objective description of the advance of life would have to be very complex: organization everywhere, by different means; a more localized consciousness. Then, to try to explain evolution *by* the psychical nature of the stuff of the universe really becomes a very tricky business, although, at the start, such an explanation no doubt contains a sound idea. We shall retain the view that it is probably impossible fully to explain evolutionary gravity without including, in some form or other, the Within of things—not

[1] *P*, 146.

exactly psychism, but an aspect of matter that is not mechanistic.

There is in nature something like a power of invention, but it is our idea of invention that we must overhaul; we tend to compare it with the creative phenomenon produced in our consciousness, and then imagine that there is a little consciousness at the origin of life—which is not so. We must try to imagine an invention of an entirely different type.[1] Is it even to be compared with an unreflecting instinct which, quite unwittingly, turns in just that direction that will lead to the best results?[2] We cannot be sure; for explanations may be sought among the forces of electricity and chemistry (modified by the delicate and very special structure of living tissues); among hormones, the gropings of matter, in vital concurrence, and even in mathematical physics (Meyer). Whatever the outcome, we are brought back once more to the mystery of matter and its innermost properties—a mystery that will one day be cleared up. If we continue along this line, we shall come to conceive of a quite new type of invention or constructive power—one that is probably not

[1] This idea has been expressed by André Tétry. Cf. "Outillage animal et techniques humaines", in *Psychisme animal et âme humaine*, Spes, 1954, p. 96.

[2] The *vis aestimativa* of Aristotle was of this kind—the faculty of knowing beforehand, through some presentiment, what will be useful and what harmful.

psychical: that is to say, one that opposes all psychism (and even blind instinct) more than it resembles it. When we can begin to define this method of discovery that is endowed with organizing ability, and, with it, all its characteristics, we shall have taken a long stride forward.

The above remark, like many that have gone before, is less an adverse criticism of Teilhard than a statement of the problem. He did, no doubt, tend more than was justified to close the gap between human invention and that which, in living species, looks like invention. But we get a strong impression that he was on the track of some reality, even if his formulae or his ideas do not wholly do it justice. He detected a certain property of life, revealed in the co-ordination of the elements of an organism; this property he also took to be responsible for the evolutionary impetus, for co-ordination takes place by successive stages, beginning with vague outlines which later grow more definite, more precise. This property of life should be studied without any romanticism, and examined by all the means open to us. It has not, up to the present, been possible to determine the nature of, or the part played by, biological invention (if "invention" is the right word).

5

OTHER VIEWS

MANY people, when they read Teilhard de Chardin, get the impression that he has proved his case. This, they feel, is how things are, and one cannot, unless one is dishonest, see them otherwise. But it is, on the contrary, a good thing to see how much there is in his argument that is not self-evident. Faced by the facts as they are, we have several approaches open to us; we must only decide on one, and discard all the others, when we have gone very thoroughly into our reasons for doing so.

Once we have established the fact of one tendency, one trend, of the whole (and this, by and large, is now beyond discussion), we can look for the most restricted explanation of it—the explanation that entails the fewest hypotheses. This is what Simpson, for instance, does. It certainly seems possible to find an explanation for the change of one sub-species or species into another, without having to introduce a systematic cause other than natural selection, variations of habitat, and other fairly humble factors. Not

that it is easy to follow the complex interplay of
mutations, the splitting up of groups, competi-
tions, migrations, changes of climate. But we are
on a track that may lead us far, and on which we
find an extraordinary amount that is intelligible,
and which moreover is based on a foundation
of ascertained fact; for we know that there have
been such things as changes of habitat, the splitting up of groups of animals, and so on.[1] We
shall try, therefore, to explain major evolutions
by similar processes—mutations, selection, the
influence of background, and possibly, in so far
as experience supports it, a certain interior
impetus such as Lamarck believed in. We shall
show how small results, due to chance or the
interplay of precedent causes, are used in such a
way as to lead on to further progress; how a
more complex organization comes gradually into

[1] This, for instance, is how Simpson explains the
appearance, among horses, of a herbivorous group. To
begin with, all horses ate leaves. Their teeth became
steadily longer in comparison with their width (hypsodonty); this slow, regular lengthening of the teeth
followed (by selection) an increase in the animals'
height, for teeth that are long in proportion to their
width help tall animals to survive. (Tall animals, which
eat more, in proportion to their height, than small ones,
wear out their teeth more quickly.) In certain cases,
mutations led to the teeth being too long—longer than
the optimum length; in other cases, the teeth were too
short. These latter put their owner at a decided disadvantage as regards selection, whereas the most hypsodontic animals were hardly at a disadvantage, for

being over long stretches of time; and how
powers once acquired become potentialities
opening the way to fresh advance. The first tentative beginnings, if they come off, are selected
and retained by nature, to become the seedbed
for future variations. A kind of trap system is
thus set up by the pitiless laws of life, with the
aim of eliminating variations that cannot adapt
themselves, and favouring those with a future
before them. Selection thus plays a really creative
part, deciding as it does in each generation the
types of organism that are to form the generation
that will follow. Selection builds up organisms
that are increasingly well adapted to the conditions of life at that particular moment. The
detail is highly complicated. But, taking it on a
whole, we may hope to be able to account for
the facts without appealing to causes remote

---

excessive length of teeth was unnecessary rather than
actually harmful. Moreover, a new possibility became
open to them—they could eat grass, which, being very
abrasive to the teeth, was ruled out as far as normal
horses were concerned. It was, to begin with, an extra
in the diet of the most hypsodontic individual horses.
But, for this reason, a new trend in selection favoured
exaggerated hypsodonty (exaggerated, that is to say, for
leaf-eaters). Thus there were born animals so highly
hypsodontic as to be adapted for grazing, and for
making grass, at first their main, and later their sole,
form of food. And in this way the world of horses split
into two distinct groups. A minor rectilinear evolution
had taken place. (See Simpson, *Tempo and Mode in
Evolution*, p. 209.)

from experience. If this type of explanation is valid, there is no such thing as evolutionary gravity, properly speaking. There is a kind of statistical law of accumulation of effects; this leads, certainly, to a general trend in living forms; but no force, physical or psychical, to be compared with that of gravity; no force extending throughout evolution as a whole does in fact supervene.

Teilhard's theories are, then, reduced to their outer appearance, and lose their true range. It is still possible that there is a Within of things, but the part that it plays in evolution is negligible. We are obviously witnessing a gradual rise of psychisms, but there is no cause which produces them systematically; nor is there, in nature, a call to consciousness, nor any impetus which urges to it; there is not, except metaphorically speaking, any evolutionary force. This being so, it is idle to try to define a general formula or line of advance, and thereby hope to obtain a preview of the evolution of the future. There is no universal law that we can extrapolate, or that will provide us with deep philosophical meanings. The factors at work were extremely varied; they do not all act in the same way; we may, indeed, forecast, for a very short time to come, what is to happen next, by making a close analysis of what is happening now; but the future cannot be deduced from a general law to which all evolutionary progress is subject.

It is, of course, arguable that the current synthetic theory of Fischer, Haldane, Sewall
Wright, Julian Huxley, Simpson and others, is
not enough to explain the facts as we know them.
But it is incumbent on us to prove this logically. Simpson studies experimental data with
the most scrupulous care; he tests the various
interpretations; his inductions stick closely to
the facts; he introduces quantitative considerations; he sets an excellent example of scientific
method (which makes Teilhard's generosity look
somewhat irresponsible). If we propose to discuss
him, we must do so on the same high level. Are
we to imagine, over and above the causes which
he recognizes, a systematic factor of another
order? The question is extremely complex. It
seems that there is an inner impetus (Simpson
allows for it), for mutations do not take place
to an equal extent in all possible directions;
there is often one main direction—clearly
marked, at times—to be seen. But the direction
really followed by evolution is not that.[1] Therefore, the interior drive shown by the inequality
of mutations is not the cause of evolutionary progress; or else it is kept in check by other factors
which play a more decisive part.

This leads us to look to selection for our explanation, rather than to any interior factor. On
the other hand, selection seems to take no hand

[1] Simpson, p. 156.

at all in every case in which some new characteristic is barely discernible.

"A horn has selective value when well developed, but will an increase in its size be favoured by selection when it is barely incipient? ... Such examples, which are very numerous, are standard items of evidence in favour of an inherent factor of some sort in orthogenesis independent of selection."[1]

But observations have shown that slight modifications have at times very obvious consequences as regards adaptation and selection.

In support of the theory of a systematic cause controlling the entire process of evolution, Teilhard declares:

> The impetus of the world, glimpsed in the great drive of consciousness, can only have its ultimate source in some *inner* principle, which alone could explain its irreversible advance towards higher psychisms.[2]

It is an intuition that may be right. It expresses in a simple, direct, perhaps artless manner what is in fact the impression of every palaeontologist who, watching the unfolding of life on a miniature scale, is quick to liken it to the growth of a seed. Nevertheless, a trap-system should give roughly the same results as an inner drive towards the greatest possible efficacy of

[1] Simpson, p. 156.
[2] *P,* 149.

living things. I am not, of course, claiming that
a trap-system is enough to explain all the facts,
but it must be admitted that the contrary conclusion is not established, and that it calls for
very strong proof. And if there is an inner principle, the whole question is, what principle?

Meyer puts forward an original argument in
favour of there being a systematic cause. I should
like to say a few words about this theory, for it is
strangely enlightening to compare it with that
of Teilhard. At first sight, the two concepts
look alike; they have, indeed, many extremely
important points in common; yet how very different is their spirit and method! A glance at
Meyer's theory will bring out the characteristics
peculiar to Teilhard's approach.

Meyer holds that micro-causalities are not
enough to account for macro-phenomena—in the
order, that is to say, of the general ascent of
evolution, whose characteristics are so clearly
marked. We cannot explain a forest as we can
a tree. There are some laws which are on the
scale of detail, and other laws which are on the
scale of history. Thus, the growth of the human
population since the beginning of the seven-
teenth century (when the first serious observations were carried out) can be shown by a regular
and sharply rising curve, which would not be
perceptible if we studied only individual causes
(always so very variable) of a psychical or

psychological order. There is such a thing as macro-cosmic truth which deserves our attention.

We must, no doubt, admit that local causes —epidemics, wars, the phenomena of demographic depression—have caused the detail of the curve to fluctuate in its ascent; but these fluctuations are none the less wholly contained within an *enveloping curve* that can be clearly identified as a macroscopic phenomenon.[1]

In the same way evolution, when seen on a large enough scale, obeys structural laws which small causes cannot account for. Meyer studies a certain number of curves, all having the same rate of ascent and all verifying the same type of equation. They prove, not only that there is a pattern of evolution as a whole, but that this pattern is quite distinctive. The curves ascend in a characteristic way. Neither this form, nor the corresponding equation, is to be seen in natural phenomena when they are due to chance variations, becoming gradually accentuated, without any systematic cause.[2] It seems, then, that the

[1] François Meyer, *Problématique de l'évolution*, P.U.F., 1954, p. 63.

[2] In such cases, if we presuppose an accumulation at a constant rate, an exponential is often obtained. But the equation of the evolutionary curves is of another type: $(l - e^{-at})^{-n}$, time being reckoned positively towards the past, starting from an epoch 1 which is set in a near future. Cf. F. Meyer, *Problématique de l'évolution*, p. 73.

We should, however, note that it is very difficult to

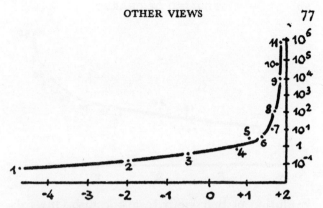

Technical Progress: Motive Power in H.P.
(Time in thousands of years)

(1) Man.   (2) Ass.   (3) Ox.   (4) Horse.   (5) Watermill.
(6) Fixed windmill.   (7) Rotatory Windmill.   (8) Watt's
steam engine.   (9) and (10) Marine steam engine.
(11) Modern electrical generator.

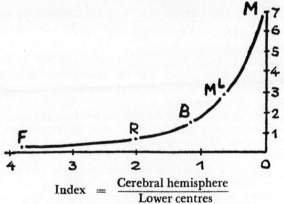

$$\text{Index} = \frac{\text{Cerebral hemisphere}}{\text{Lower centres}}$$

Fish, Reptile, Bird, Mammal, Man.
(Time in hundreds of millions of years)

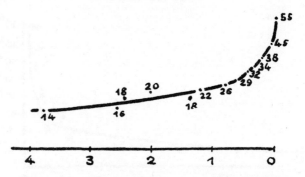

Evolution of Behaviour from the Fish Onwards.
(Time in hundreds of millions of years)
(after Cailleux)

To see how the scale was determined, see F. Meyer,
Problématique de l'évolution, pp. 134–6. The above
diagrams are taken from this work, pp. 67, 125, 135.

"dip" in the curves does not correspond to accidental successes retained and made use of by a
trap-system.

---

formulate an equation for the mechanisms described
by Simpson and to be sure that they do not correspond
to the curves obtained.

One contrast seems clear enough; there are cases of
progression at a constant rate, such as the increase of
the number of species: on the other hand, the stages of
anatomical development and psychism in the course
of geological history, human demography and indus-
tries, seem to correspond to an increasing rate. Cf.
Cailleux, in *Bull. Soc. préhistorique française*, 50, nos.
9–10, 1953, p. 512: and *La Géologie*, P.U.F., p. 124
(series "Que sais-je?").

This would be a very strong argument if the line of the curves were beyond dispute. But there is a touch of the arbitrary in the way they are read. On the whole, however, the argument is sound enough.

The idea of a law of the whole resulting from a systematic factor links up with the evolutionary "gravity" suggested by Teilhard de Chardin. Again, there is complete agreement over this principle of explanation: "We are led to enquire whether, contrary to all likelihood, there is not some necessary connection between cosmic evolution, and biological."[1]

It should be added that entropic phenomena (i.e., phenomena of increasing entropy), and the phenomena of life, are complementary. Against the processes of divergence, of decline into the most probable, of advance towards confusion, which together fall to the share of the universe, are the processes of life in evolution, all tending to convergence, and raising up increasingly improbable structures. Père Teilhard de Chardin, agreeing on this point with Meyer, once asserted at a scientific meeting that "there is something that arranges, converges, becomes concentrated, interiorized, develops corpuscles—*through* something else that disarranges, diverges, expands and loses its corpuscles."[2]

[1] Meyer, p. 248.
[2] Meeting of the Union catholique des scientifiques français, bulletin no. 25, March–April 1955.

But at once, after this, the divergence begins. It would be of little moment if it concerned only Meyer's mathematical exposition. We can understand Teilhard's putting biological considerations above a physico-mathematical theory, although the latter has an essential part to play if biological evolution is to be related to the evolution of the cosmos. But this is not the crux of the matter. It is possible to criticize the details of Meyer's reasoning, and none the less carry out our enquiry in the same spirit, understand the nature of the scientific explanation in the same way, and look to physics proper for the systematic factor in evolution. The factor that Meyer suggests is, indeed, not psychical; and this wide divergence from Teilhard's views indicates an entirely different type of search for intelligibility. And if Meyer is right, it will have to be shown by what mechanisms the improbable structures of the syntropic wave become biological effects (or psychism). There is an enormous amount of work still to be done here.

We cannot say that the spring of life is the same, whether we decide on psychical causes or a wave of improbability; the distinctive line of action of the psychic forces is quite differently conceived in the two cases. But the choice between the two is not so much the result of technical study; it depends above all on our mental attitude towards the facts. This is what I want, step by step, to bring out.

Meyer adopts and modifies a theory put forward by the Italian, Fantappiè, which concludes to the physical existence of processes in which the entropy decreases. Entropic phenomena (phenomena in which entropy—i.e., disorder—is increasing) are those with which we are most familiar; everything wears out, everything tends, by its very nature, to disorder and disintegration. These phenomena correspond to what are known as "retarded" actions—actions, that is, wherein the cause precedes and determines the effect. It is often argued that such actions alone are possible in our universe.[1] We should, however, recognize that actions of the opposite type, those known as "advanced" actions, are physically possible.

Let us try to see and understand what the advance action suggested by this theory consists in (assuming, of course, that it exists at all). If "retarded" action seems quite clear to us, it may be because, where cause precedes effect, our own minds work in the same order as the phenomena, deducing cause from effect, and tracing the development of the physical process from the very first instant. Thus, Henri Poincaré studies the distribution of small planets from the moment of their breaking away from the

[1] And the second solution of D'Alembert's equation, which corresponds to "advance" actions, is regarded as purely theoretical—i.e., without any physical significance.

nebulae. This example shows us a characteristic property of delayed actions; they tend, unless something from without interferes with them, towards states of increasing probability; small planets end by being strewn at random all over the heavens.[1] "Retarded" action implies a tendency to the probable, or, again, an increase of entropy.[2]

Henri Poincaré borrows from Flammarion the figure of an imaginary observer, Lumen, to whom time goes backwards; and describes the surprises that lie in wait for him. Instead of seeing a warm body and a cold body adjust their temperatures to one another, he sees temperatures becoming differentiated in an amazing manner. "He would see an increasingly varied world emerging from primeval chaos; the changes he observed would be, where he was concerned, unforeseen and wholly unforeseeable."[3] The lava strewn round a volcano would again coalesce within the crater. Out of a heap of ashes would arise the Paris Charity Bazaar.

Can phenomena comparable with this backward-working vision be foreseen from our present knowledge of physics? The irreversi-

[1] H. Poincaré, *Science et méthode*, Flammarion, 1916, p. 70.

[2] Cf. Costa de Beauregard, "L'Irréversibilité quantique, phénòmene macroscopique", in *Louis de Broglie, physicien et penseur*, Albin Michel.

[3] H. Poincaré, *Science et méthode*, p. 70.

bility that characterizes every process is a statistical law only; there is complete symmetry between past and future in the individual phenomena at the quantum level. The trend towards the probable is a law of the whole, but not a law of the element.

Once this elementary symmetry has been granted, we find it conceivable that, in circumstances as yet unknown, some macroscopic phenomenon may show the characteristics of "advance" action.

If this ever comes to pass, what shall we find? Like Flammarion's observer, Lumen, we shall see highly differentiated states gradually combining from an almost homogeneous initial datum. The phenomena seem to be drawn by some future magnet. Physical causes are determined by their final effect. And these appearances are explained—fully explained, on the scientific level—by a purely physical action.

If it is true that, by the nature of the cosmos, "advance" actions are possible, we must not be afraid to say that they actually take place in the evolution of life.

Meyer claims to prove that such actions are possible; this, he holds, can be deduced with absolute certainty from a mathematical formula based on the wave-corpuscle-relativity structure. But there are certain weak links in his deduction which lessen the strength of the whole. The expansion of the universe, by dispersing the

elements, is tending towards states that are more
and more probable. Meyer thinks that this is
made up for by a counter-movement which produces states less probable than their predecessors.
Heisenberg's relations prove that there is a compensation of improbability for an elementary
particle and the wave associated with it.[1] Gener-
alizing from this law, Meyer applies it, in a way
that seems open to argument, to the beings of
the stellar universe. He breaks clean away from
the specific line along which Heisenberg's relations lend themselves to exact deductions. He
assumes that the mathematical formalism in
which they are expressed has a far wider range
than the limited example by which it has been
proved. It is an interesting argument, but the

---

[1] Whereas the position of the wave is strictly defined,
that of the corpuscle is defined only by a law of probability; its speed is one of the speeds corresponding to
the various monochromatic constituents of the wave.
If the area of the corpuscle's possible presence contracts
(in which case the probability of its presence increases),
the number of monochromatic constituents is aug-
mented; the greater certainty over position is made up
for by greater uncertainty over speed.

If the area of possible presence of the corpuscle
grows, its probability diminishes; this is counter-
balanced by a better knowledge of speed. Meyer, however, adopting the diametrically opposed view, sees the
greatest probability in the state of greatest dispersion,
and makes up for it by a law of unforeseeability.
Heisenberg's relations never meant that. There is, then,
it seems to me, a radical difference of interpretation.

working hypothesis resulting from it needs to be subjected to prolonged testing by both physics and biology.

Louis de Broglie, discussing the concepts of Bohr, Jordan and Fantappiè regarding "advanced" actions, declared: "These are certainly very daring views: they give rise to many objections, and will not, perhaps, have a lasting place in science. But the mere fact that it has been possible seriously to propound them is in itself a warning."[1]

What interests us in such a hypothesis is the *type of explanation* that it calls forth. On the one hand it tries to discover a systematic cause of evolution, one showing that the appearance of a concerted plan may be the result of a natural factor (irrespective of whether there was, at the beginning of the world, some controlling mind). And on the other hand it seeks this factor in mathematical physics; in this capacity it forms a fixed point, a limiting hypothesis, the extremity of one possible line of explanation. Teilhard took the exactly opposite approach, making the most of anything in nature that may be compared with psychism. This is what makes the contrast so interesting. We understand Teilhard better when we compare him with Meyer and Simpson.

[1] "Qu'est ce que la vie"? in *Les Nouvelles littéraires*, 2 March 1950. François Meyer's book had not yet appeared.

Meyer writes in his conclusion:

> To carry the constituents of the objective universe to the last point conceivable at a certain definite stage of knowledge; to reject all explanation of phenomena by spirit; even to do that, we have to live the life of the spirit —to live fearlessly that adventure of knowledge without which the spirit dies away.[1]

All that is in question is the scientific explanation (a definite stage of knowledge); but it is precisely at this stage that Teilhard takes up his position. Meyer holds that human intelligence is completely true to its own law and the law of things only when it brushes aside all explanations based on spirit. It is easy to see the reason for this principle; things are not made like the human spirit, and we should be very seriously thrown out were we to overlook this difference. If the intelligence is to do its work, it must be objective; it must see in physical reality what are in fact its processes—not read into them those of thought. Physical reality is intelligible; it can, *as object*, coincide with thought, but it is not the subject—in other words, it is not the source of any life that can be identified with the life of thought. Doubtless, when we speak of biological realities, the real datum is indeed the source of a certain life, which acts by a sort of inner gushing, comparable, up to a point, with the action

[1] *Problématique*, p. 278.

of spirit. But the resemblance, for all that, is a fairly rough one, and we have to bear in mind both the likeness and the discrepancies—which is what makes biological thinking so difficult.

We shall, then, accept Meyer's principle ·in this sense: the mind must endeavour to understand physical reality as it is, and, especially, as being the source of processes which are not those of spirit (even·though they are somewhat like them).

Teilhard seeks the explanation of matter in an impulse of matter that is related to spirit—a most mysterious impulse, gifted with the ability to prefer consciousness or brain to everything else, and which has even a plan all ready for human development, just as it once controlled the destiny of animal evolution. Meyer, in his explanation of the same facts, introduces a calculable syntropic wave; and tries to prove that this is closely connected, by Heisenberg's relations, with the expansion of the universe. The difference between the two methods is startling.

Does Meyer lay himself open to the reproach of not fully understanding the originality of the biological facts? Perhaps not, for quantitative relations do exist, and we must be on the lookout for them. But an explanation of this sort will not be complete until a great deal more biological research has gone into it. We can be sure, *a priori*, that Meyer has not said the last word on the subject. But there is in him a love of accuracy and concern for objectivity which it would be a pity to lose.

In judging of the validity of either approach, we have to ask ourselves whether "advanced" actions have not a special affinity to spirit; if we decide that this is so, we shall have, on Meyer's own claims, to reintroduce into physical reality a sort of initiative comparable with that of spirit.

Obviously, "advanced" actions, if they are at work in evolution, do bring about psychism, do lead to perception and invention. But a cause is not necessarily of the same nature as its effect. As a cosmic process, "advanced" action is a physical phenomenon like any other, similar to the expansion of the universe. A macroscopic process takes place, in one direction or the other, as a result of sheer necessities within the physical order; and there is no need to bring in a spiritual element at all.[1]

---

[1] At least on the scientific level. The philosophical question remains unchanged. We should ask ourselves what metaphysical conditions there would have to be, assuming advance actions, to make the universe possible. Is the universe an instrument—i.e., contrived by a first thought? The question also arises, and in just the same way, over "retarded" actions.

Whether the universe is instrumental or not, the working of mechanisms, which is the one concern of science, remains exactly the same; and—on this level—the explanation does not change.

At this point Teilhard would perhaps reply, "Oh, certainly—it is the universe, and the universe alone, that counts for anything in the scientific explanation. But the whole point is that the universe is by nature psychical. This is not visible in other fields; but in biological phenomena it can be seen very clearly."

But we have to consider the stuff of the universe—i.e., physical reality with all its properties, before the appearance of life on earth (or on any star). At that time there was not, anywhere in the universe, such a thing as invention or perception (unless we misuse words. The first sketchy outlines of these phenomena which Teilhard deduces should not be called imagination or perception). Yet the great process of "advanced" actions was on the way. They have no more connection with spirit than have "retarded" actions.

Teilhard and Meyer are both preoccupied by one problem: How is life to be integrated into the cosmos? How are the currents of entropy and life, which seem to be direct opposites, to be brought into the unity of a cosmic history? In answering this difficulty, Meyer speaks of a law of compensation of probabilities; he defines, very sharply, the anti-chance character of vital phenomena.[1] The law of compensation that he tries to prove may be open to grave doubt, but

[1] *Problématique*, p. 204-14.

4+

it speaks of a quest for intelligibility which is purely scientific, in the truest sense of the word. Teilhard—in certain passages, anyway—adopts quite a different approach to the same question. He plumps for a sort of pan-psychism, a continuity between matter and invention, an affinity between cosmic forces and the powers of our spirit. Believing, like Meyer, in a systematic cause prompting the general direction of life, he seems to oscillate between two wholly dissimilar explanations. Let us examine them separately.

First hypothesis. Evolutionary "gravity" is something purely physical. The advance of life is bound up with such phenomena as the distribution of the stars, the formation of corpuscles "under the action of electro-magnetic and gravitational forces", or their "dematerialization in radiation",[1] a telluric process of chemical modification, a maturation of the biosphere that transcends individuals.[2] In this way complex organisms, endowed with psychical powers, come to be formed. But the evolutionary process, considered in its causes, is no more psychical than some phenomenon of electricity or radio-activity. There is, indeed, a "within" of things, but this is already at work in chemistry or magnetism. It is slightly more active in living phenomena, especially towards the end of evolution: from

[1] P, 301.
[2] V, 152, cf. 153 and 68.

the time of man's appearance, it is more active still. Right down to our day, and even in the case of the higher animals, it plays but a restricted part in evolution, introducing shades of distinction rather than anything more definite.

Second hypothesis. The rudimentary psychism of the material universe is trying—confusedly, yet psychically—to improve—whether through individuals, or through the biosphere as a whole, or whether, on a wider scale still, the world feels the mysterious pull of higher psychisms, and, finally, in some way that is never very clearly explained, is drawn by the attraction of the Omega-Point. Such a concept does not, of course, rule out the cosmic or telluric processes of the former theory, but it adds to it (making it, perhaps, their source?) a phenomenon of a completely different order.

This second hypothesis is certainly not one to be dismissed out of hand; despite its suggestion of the mythological, it may well, in its own way, be expressing a truth. But, in the absence of any conclusive argument, to say nothing of experimental corroboration, it would seem gratuitous. And, when the first hypothesis meets the case, it would go against the grain to a scientist to admit the second. It is not even certain that the first itself is necessary, since the factors described by Simpson—or others like them—provide a good enough explanation. As for the second hypothesis, what can be said in its favour? On the scientific level, there does not seem to be one really strong argument. Is there any evidence for it outside science? This is a question that we shall have to look into.

Teilhard did not, perhaps, openly choose between the two hypotheses. We need not hold it against him that he gave no definite answer to a problem which no-one has as yet fully mastered. His observations on universal psychism (it would be better to speak of universal preparations for psychism) have certainly some truth in them. But the point is not to decide whether there is any psychism—in the vegetable kingdom, for instance. Almost certainly there is (there is a pre-psychism); what we have to find out is whether this factor guides evolution. And it is to be feared that Teilhard greatly exaggerates the part it plays. One hesitates to say that he was wrong, for every now and then one comes on formulas that are certainly true; but often the confused way in which he expresses himself makes it impossible to tell where the thought breaks off; and the underlying suggestions leave the reader feeling troubled and disappointed. One would have liked Teilhard to show a little more self-criticism, to draw up a more concise balance-sheet of his assertions, estimating their relative degrees of certainty, and drawing a clear distinction between the cosmological (hyper-physical), the philosophical, and the religious. We admire, indeed, his breadth of vision, and certain subjects very suitable for meditation stick in our minds; but the meditation is in its first stages and needs to be carried further.

6

THE PROLONGATION OF EVOLUTION

EVER since the first appearance of man, consciousness has played a decisive part, not only in the everyday activities of life, but in the evolutionary process itself. According to Teilhard de Chardin, the evolution of the species is continued by the history of man, and this continuation is no branching-off, but a steady advance along the same line. Yet a new force, that of the human spirit, has come into play. If, as Teilhard thinks, the "step of reflection" corresponds with a real change of state, this force is of an entirely new nature.

As regards this change of state, which may be illustrated by a physical (or hyper-physical) image at the phenomenal level, we may accept the excellent comparison suggested by Teilhard: when water begins to boil, the slightest increase in the heat causes a considerable change in the phenomenon.[1] In the same way, the psychical functioning of a human being is entirely different from that of an animal, in spite of the biological continuity between them (that is to

[1] *P*, 168.

say, no doubt, the fairly slight variation of a mutation). That the ordinary man today does not think in the same way as do animals seems to me quite clear from any serious philosophical description of the fact of intelligence. We have reached the limit of what can appertain to scientific reflection; for, true though it is that the psychological is a part of this generalized scientific reflection; for, true though it is that type is needed in order to recognize the nature of thought. We shall not, therefore, discuss this question, which is certainly a very delicate one. We admit that there is in fact an intellectual functioning which is peculiar to man.[1] Was

[1] It is not easy to describe this functioning. It is true, no doubt, that man is able to know that he knows (V, 371), and we can speak of consciousness raised to a higher power (A, 314, 317); but these expressions do not carry us very far. Above all, we must not say that thought takes "possession of itself *as of an object*" (P, 165), for the whole point is that thought does not in the least know itself as an object, but subjectively, from within; and that is precisely what human consciousness is. In the act of knowing some object, thought can become conscious of itself (as an intellectual act) by auto-transparency. In knowing the object, it transcends it, not only by this intuition of itself, but by its ability to *place* the object. It goes beyond immediate perception: it forms universal concepts, seeks out the essential and distinguishes it from the contingent. The grasp of *necessity* is perhaps its most characteristic feature. Finally, under various aspects, thought can stand at a distance both from the concrete fact and from its own perception.

there, or was there not, a progressive transition
from simian psychology to the first human reflection? From what phenomena have to tell us, the
answer is uncertain; documentation is, of course,
lacking, and contemporary introspection does
not, perhaps, prove the necessity for any clearly-
defined "threshold".[1] But this is of little importance to the matter under discussion.

It is possible that henceforth the human brain
will not change, or will change very little. But
humanity will continue its advance, for the
sapiens group is still very young.[2] A passage in
one of Teilhard's works gives us an excellent
summing-up of how he sees the evolution of the
future, and also of how he connects it with the
earlier phases; it will, I think, be helpful to
give the gist of what he says:

> The march of time can (should) be meas-
> ured by an increasing concentration of
> matter, which becomes haloed by an ever-
> growing light of freedom and consciousness.
> All down the ages, consciousness on earth has
> grown unceasingly, as the direct result of a
> more advanced organization of elements which
> themselves become increasingly complicated

[1] Teilhard is undoubtedly jumping his guns when
he tells us that reflection can "only be achieved *at one
single stroke*". (*P*, 171.) It may not be impossible for
an anthropoid to come gradually to stand back from its
perceptions. This is a point that should be held over.
[2] *A*, 173.

—elements built up by chemical and living energies.

... Man stands as the (earthly) head of a universe which is continually moving on to higher states of consciousness. Man is the last to be formed, and the highest, of the "molecules".

... The world has advanced *at least as far as ourselves*. This is one of the first points which it is important for us to remember. But we must now carry the journey further. Life, in its evolution, has culminated in man: agreed. But now that it has reached this stage, has it called a halt? Life has been stirring, up to the time when thought came into being: we accept this fact; but, from that time onward, has it gone any further—car it go any further?

Humanity is still very young ... Yet ... even over a period as short as this, it seems possible (at least for a practised eye) to trace the advance of our group through consciousness.

(a) In the first place, it certainly seems as though, anatomically speaking, a progress of the brain may be observed throughout the earliest phases of our "phylo-genesis". Peking Man was intelligent; but we have very good reasons for thinking that he was not as highly "developed" as ourselves.

4*

(b) With the appearance of what anthropologists call "homo sapiens", it certainly seems as though our modern brain had finished with construction; or at any rate, if it has changed since then, the modification is not as yet perceptible. On the other hand, if no anatomical progress is discernible in bodies (or even in individual psychical faculties) since the Reindeer (or Cave) Age, a *collective psychical progress* is beyond all question: and this, too, is a real progress—and, moreover, along the main line of progress.

... Progress = rise of consciousness.

Rise of consciousness = the phenomenon of organization—i.e., of concentration (which varies with the degree of organization).

... Is it not obvious that in the last twenty or twenty-five thousand years (from the Reindeer Age), mankind has made astounding advances in its organization?

In economic organization—the unifying of earth's energies:

In intellectual organization—the unifying of all branches of knowledge in a coherent system—science:

In social organization—the unifying of the human mass in a thinking whole.

... The two curves prolong each other ... How is this new order which everyone is

talking about to be recognized, if not in mankind's increased consciousness of itself—
mankind grown both more complex and more
centralized?[1]

In trying to learn the future of evolution,
Teilhard applies what he believes to be a
universal law—the increase of complexity-
consciousness. If this is indeed the key to the
universe; if it does express the unfaltering trend
of its advance; we may conclude that mankind
is on the way to a higher degree of consciousness
and arrangement. If we grant that the organism
and, in particular, the brain, have no further
evolution before them, there nevertheless still
remains the organization of the planetary community.

This reasoning leads Teilhard to two successive conclusions:

(1) Human organization is a continuation of
morphological evolution.

(2) It will culminate in a superorganism made
up of individuals, just as the individual is made
up of cells.

The first of these conclusions does not present
any difficulties; as long as it is left fairly vague—
no more than a general indication—I think it is
far-reaching and true: indeed, it may well be

[1] "L'Avenir de l'homme, vues d'un paléontologiste",
in *Cité nouvelle*, 10 June 1941.

(apart from technical works on human palaeontology) the most significant contribution that Père Teilhard de Chardin has to make. But the second conclusion seems far more open to question. The extrapolation that predicts a superorganism—i.e., in the strict sense of the words, a change of state for mankind—seems very rash, and runs us at once into uncertainties. Let us look more closely at what it forecasts.

If our knowledge did not extend beyond animal evolution and the rise of the human species, and if we knew nothing of the direction in which mankind has advanced since it first began to exist, we should not even have any grounds for believing in the collective development of the human mind. Teilhard's extrapolation depends on the truth of an assumption —the assumption that any future development will always be homogeneous with that which preceded it—that is to say, of the same nature and tending more or less in the same direction. But an aeroplane which has been going in a straight line may change its course; it may climb or come down. A phylum may die out[1]; or it may undergo mutations; there are innumerable ways in which it may become diversified, and perhaps the twig furthest from the centre will

---

[1] In the next chapter, we shall study Teilhard's argument concerning the infallible nature of the evolutionary movement, and the utter impossibility that it should ever come to grief.

be the only one to blossom. In the early days of mankind, many hypotheses were possible. Today—if we take into account the history that man already has behind him, and do not try to look too far into the future—these hypotheses are fewer. And this means that hardly any extrapolation is possible.

Seen in this light, Teilhard's reasoning, at least as regards his first conclusion, is based on very sound arguments. He studied speciation (the diversification of a living group into new species) both in animal series and in the very special case of man. When it is indeed the naturalist who speaks, he has an enormous amount to teach us—and Teilhard has a keen sense of human natural history. The human group is not diversified, as are the others. Among animals, the diverging lines go further and further from one another, so that they cannot intersect; whereas, in man, interfecundity still persists, the ramifications forming a fan, and the veins a network.[1] The diversity of the branches is used in such a way as to lead, by means of combinations, to higher forms of consciousness.[2] "The most humanized human collectivities always appear finally as the product, not of segregation, but of synthesis."[3] Cultural unities react on one another (acculturation) and lead to an improvement in quality. In man, culturation

[1] *V*, 286.   [2] *V*, 291.
[3] *V*, 291.

amounts to the same thing as speciation,[1] which means that human speciation is not only divergent, but in one sense tends to converge. Or again—but this comes to the same thing—true unity differentiates; the human species seems by its nature destined, on the one hand to explore all possible avenues of cultural enquiry, and on the other, by pooling its treasures and thus heightening the general consciousness, to unite in its very diversity.

If we believe that morphological evolution has come to a standstill and that we are now, as Rostand thinks, in a period of agenesis, there is, none the less, a "human rebound of evolution". The inventions of our brains take the place of the natural renewal of forms; we don't grow wings, but we make aeroplanes. Moreover, man will probably learn to perfect his own nervous system—through guided selection, for instance.[2] He will call forth life in hitherto unknown forms, endowing the earth with "a new wave of organisms".[3] By thinking "the world" he will confer upon it a unique form of unity, and a new perfection.[4]

But we cannot rule out the possibility of mankind's going off on quite a different track, which would effectively disrupt the magnificent unitary plan outlined by Teilhard de Chardin.

[1] V, 374, 376.
[3] P, 250.
[2] A, 351.
[4] P, 249, n. 2.

Biology may, perhaps, manage to produce supermen who "would be to us as we are to prehistoric man".[1] Has natural evolution itself quite done with transforming us?

Without stepping outside the sphere of individual anatomy, there is nothing to prove (far from it, indeed) that important evolutionary potentialities (some more advanced arrangement of nervous fibres) are not still held in reserve in the substance of our brains.[2]

Were phenomena of this sort to occur, they might lead to a *dispersion* of human nature, of which at present we have no idea. Teilhard takes due note that there are in nature two kinds of development: orthogenesis, which leads to a completed type such as the series mammals, primates, man, and fan-like mutations, which end in dispersion.[3] At the present moment, as far as man is concerned, the forces of psychical unification seem (if all goes well) strong enough to dominate the causes of biological differentiation. But were we to enter on a phase of "spectrum-like" diversification, the plan for unification could probably never be carried out. But, to be quite honest, we have nothing but hypotheses to go on, and cannot see ahead into any future that is at all remote.

[1] Rostand, p. 49.   [2] *V*, 358.
[3] *V*, 338.

There are times when Teilhard argues as though he had discovered, beyond the cosmic reality, the intention hidden in the facts, or some eternal meaning which these facts could not possibly, at some later date, belie. But, if the universe is endowed only with the pre-psychism that we have agreed to grant, then it has no intention of any kind. Either we are speaking of a divine intention—and in that case, we should say so outright—or we must confine ourselves to saying that there are in the cosmos certain trends —which may alter. Before we could affirm categorically that they would always be the same, we should have to be sure that we had discovered a systematic cause that would hold good even in the future.

In this respect, the law of complexity-consciousness may let us down. It has been proved true up to the present, but this is simply an empirical result of which the real cause is unknown. Besides, it must be admitted that it makes use of the most varied technical methods. If Teilhard is right, cosmic phenomena proceed in a remarkably disjointed manner. Evolution has formed man by a morphological process culminating, notably, in the brain: then it suddenly throws up that line of development and starts off on another—collective organization, with all its psychical consequences. This is not something completely new, for vegetable and animal colonies existed before there was any life at all;

Teilhard agrees that *all* living individuals tend, in varying degrees, to associate.[1] This old and universal phenomenon now lies behind the one form of progress that is really noteworthy. How far will this road lead us? Is it out of the question that another path will be found? On the cosmological level, all we can say is that, wherever possible, the universe sets in motion all the machinery of arrangement, and this, at all stages—at the stage of the cell, the individual, society, the astral spheres, the galaxy. Life is not a blue-print, or a well-arranged conducted tour; it is full of freakish twists and turns; we must be moderate in our expectations. The current of evolution seems long ago to have slowed down and become stagnant; we may, then, hazard a guess that the chief event now will be social aggregation. This is plausible and even likely, but it is not the inevitable outcome of a law.

There is a very strong argument for the unity of the phenomena in human history and the evolution of forms. Cailleux and Meyer drew graphs illustrating the progress of man's various pre-eminences, such as his degree of motor power at different periods. Now, these graphs have the same characteristic outline as those representing the evolution of animals. They obey a similar law, expressed by an equation of the same type. The development of mankind,

[1] *A*, 330, *G*, 106.

which has taken place through his own resources (those of intelligence and collective work, in particular), constitutes either the selfsame phenomenon as that which preceded it, or another very like it.

All in all, the natural movement towards the *psychical* organization of the planet is at least one of the factors in the world's progress, and one of the most important. We owe much to Teilhard for having pointed it out, and for having connected this discovery with the main facts already known to science. An intuition within the social and cultural order, hitherto exploited by the disciples of Marx and Hegel, and stressing the advance of history, converges both with the established findings of cosmology, and (as we shall see) with a religious thesis. Not only does it add greatly to our knowledge of things, but it opens new fields for action and gives us a fresh impetus in building a world in common; a form of spiritual life, even, begins to take shape.

We accept, then, this first conclusion: the organization of a world-wide planetary community is a continuation of morphological evolution. But Teilhard does not leave it at that; this development must, he says, lead up to a real superorganism, formed by an arrangement of individuals in the same way as our bodies are formed by an arrangement of cells.[1] In the early

[1] *A*, 215.

days of mankind, it was the "point of reflection" that was decisive, and marked a change of state; in the same way, mankind will now attain a "second point of reflection . . . superior and collective".[1] Then a brain of brains[2] will come into being, and planetization will be complete.

On the whole, Teilhard rejects, where the final state of mankind is concerned, the distinction generally made between the moral person and the physical. When a certain number of human beings (each one of whom is a physical person) form a collective unity—a nation, say— they constitute, through a multiplicity of interwoven relationships, one moral person.[3] These relationships need not be purely juridical and extrinsic, for they include ties of blood, language, culture, and such factors as the sharing of the same history, and communal work done for the same end. That mankind is increasingly destined to form a unity of this sort, seems fairly obvious. That it will one day, through a change of state, become a true physical person and a personal Great Being—that is a statement far more open to doubt.

[1] *P,* 287 *n.*

[2] "Vie et planètes", in *Études,* May 1946, p. 162.

[3] We may define the person in general by a union of two characteristics: (a) a certain unity and autonomy of existence; (b) access to the level of spirit. The moral person answers to this description, but in quite a different way from the physical person.

There is, in fact, nothing to justify it but the general observation of the contraction of the universe—i.e., a progressive concentration of matter and its properties in the course of life.

If, from all that has gone before, there is one thing that stands out as proved, it is the complete and fundamental inability of the human plurality to stand out against the forces which seek to draw it back organically upon itself—those general forces of cosmic contraction which, at the zoological and historical level that we have reached, are growing more clearly defined and more accentuated under the influence of the "entry into convergence" of the world around us. On that point no doubt is possible. By the very structure of the universe, we are forced, condemned (if we are to become fully alive) to unite.[1]

It is easy to see the weak links in this chain of inference. We know very little about the "general forces of cosmic contraction"; we do not even know if there were any *general forces*, and, if so, whether they are still active. According to Rostand, the forces which built up nature are now absent from nature. How, then, can we say that they will count for anything in man's future? Rostand's assertion is, indeed, hypothetical, and should be read with a key of doubt; it is possible that the same forces are in fact still

[1] G, 157.

THE PROLONGATION OF EVOLUTION 109

at work—possible, too, that others have taken over from them; these may be quite simply the dynamisms of human psychism. This being so, it is hard to see how one can invoke "the very structure of the universe" to back up the claim to a constitutional necessity.

It is likely enough that we may have to unite if we are to become fully alive. That is an observation based on common sense, and the study of evolution, as carried out by Teilhard, gives it added weight.[1] But that does not give us the right to predict a superorganism, or a "second point of reflection". Does there really have to be an *absolute goal* for the universe, if the experiment of life is to succeed? We cannot say with any certainty either that our condition at the heart of things demands it, or that it will ever be attained. We should have to assume that the universe (or God) had decided to carry the idea of contraction as far as it would go, by boldly applying, to the last, the process of complexity-consciousness.

And, indeed, we find several passages in Teilhard's works which set out to prove that the process of evolution cannot possibly fail, and that its results must endure for ever. This "proof" (which we will go into later) seems to me to raise grave doubts.

In "Vie et planètes", Teilhard, in speaking of the "brain of brains", says, very rightly: "On

[1] For a good study of the question, see G, 124-33.

this point I cannot, of course, force your agreement", but he adds that to accept this view "is eminently satisfying to the intelligence and strengthening to the will".[1] "If men on earth, and all over the earth, are to learn to love one another, it is not enough for them all to recognize the elements of the same *something*; they must, by becoming 'planetized', be conscious of becoming—without any loss of identity—the same *someone*."[1]

This idea is satisfying to the mind, in so far as it sets the seal on Teilhard's inductions. But, to a mind which wants to stick to the facts, there is no certainty in all this. Apart from a few verbal reservations, however, Teilhard's own conviction is complete. He seems to believe that —through his study of cosmology, certainly, but going far beyond it—he has grasped the intention of God in creating the universe; he hears this intention speaking within himself and trusts the impulses of his own spirit, in harmony as it is with the fundamental law in which the creative plan is revealed.

All this is, no doubt, quite legitimate. A highly intuitive mind may, perhaps, have the right to indulge in such speculations, when they have behind them the meditations of a lifetime. It is even likely that every great mind rediscovers, as a personal unfolding, the unfolding of reality. But, even if that is so, whatever

[1] *Études*, May 1946, pp. 162, 163.

element of uncertainty there is in the results should be handled with care. In any case, we must recognize that there are times when Teilhard oversteps the frontiers of science—even when these frontiers are generously drawn.

The whole reflection on the Omega-Point, which we are now going to look at, seems to call for much the same comment.

PART 2

PHILOSOPHY

7

THE OMEGA-POINT

THE Omega-Point stands in the first place for the end of evolution, as compared with its beginning (alpha). It means, then, as Teilhard sees it, the human superorganism which will one day come into being, after the "second point of reflection". In yet a third sense, the word stands for God, the pre-existing Centre of this superorganism. Finally, it denotes Christ —Christ bound up with the cosmos, when at last he takes possession of the final human unity and supernaturalizes it.

Teilhard's thought is worked out along two lines:

(1) Evolution is infallible; it cannot miscarry; it must go through to the end of what it has set out to do. It is written within its very law that it will end up at a definite point—the point at which mankind is unified in one higher person. Everything necessary to achieve this end is, therefore, already in existence.

(2) The end would not be achieved did there not already exist a personal centre able to sum

up all consciousness within itself, and finally to unify the human superorganism.

Let us examine in turn these two stages of the argument, holding over, for the time being, the question of the cosmic Christ.

The history of the universe is interpreted as the growth of spirit. This growth must, according to Teilhard, be irreversible and its results everlasting. The whole argument rests on a hypothesis—the coherence of the universe. This hypothesis we may accept, provided it is correctly interpreted. There is a *certain* coherence in the universe, since science works; on the other hand, the existentialist theory of the absurdity of the world has something to be said for it, and the whole point is to find exactly how the two aspects fit in—to delimit one by the other. This is one of the subtlest and also one of the most important questions confronting philosophical thought today.[1]

[1] Reality is absurd, at least in the following ways. It has not the structure of our concepts (and this is something that Plato did not see); the relations of unity and diversity are different, and our logic does not coincide with real structures (this divergency does not, by the way, necessarily imply that our logic is at fault). The act of existence is not something that can be conceptualized (we can, however, understand it); it is possible that the most important realities are not objectifiable (Jaspers). Matter, on the electronic level, is probably not imaginable. Reality (especially biological reality) does not develop like a treatise; the order that it

To Teilhard, the coherence of the universe
implies or even proclaims the impossibility of
any breakdown ever occurring. What he is considering, then, is a very special kind of
coherence, and, precisely, the kind of coherence
for which there is no guarantee. "During the
hundreds of millions of years in which the
psychical temperature of earth has been rising,
without once dropping, life must have come on

---

probably verifies is never the order that we should have
taken it to be: our idea of order and harmony has to be
endlessly revised. Our knowledge is never absolute
knowledge; our theses are always at the mercy of an
antithesis; our ideal always runs the risk of being (to
some extent) given the lie by concrete things. Even in
mathematics, the axiomists' attempts at rationalization
have come up against unexpected limitations (the
theorems of Church and Gödel). The act of defining
the significance of reality lands one in appallingly
difficult problems (a fact of which Teilhard was not
fully aware). Moreover, it is uncertain whether a
system of converging meanings can be found for reality
as a whole. Is the development of the universe the
adequate development of all natures? The functions of
the body and the human spirit are probably not entirely
compatible. There is no perfect solution to the problem
of our life. Does reality always permit of an act endowed
with meaning? Contingency, and the imperfections of
the universe, reach a point which is seldom suspected;
and so on.

On the other hand, the mathematical understanding
of the universe goes very far, and even biology finds
laws. A certain—limited—absurdity co-exists with a
specific coherence.

many obstacles lying across its path . . . Now that it has achieved its full impetus, is it possible for it to fail, just in the marvellous act of reflecting on itself, right to the end"?[1]

If the universe is—even blindly—pursuing an aim; if the whole history of the cosmos is straining after one definite result—the highest possible degree of consciousness; then the coherence of the world demands that this aim should be achieved. In this case, it is clear that our choice lies between absolute optimism and absolute pessimism.[2] Either the universe fails utterly, or it succeeds. Now, it has already succeeded; we have, then, grounds for believing that it has within it the means to go on to the end. We could, it is true, entertain the hypothesis of a partial success—partial, but sufficiently striking, when we think of its achievements up to the present. We need not, however, linger over this. The weakest point of the argument lies at its root. We are to assume that the universe has one aim and one aim alone—spirit; and that the whole universe fails if the spirit is balked of its natural desires. All that has been said in chapters 4 and 5 about the mainspring of life shows how tenuous this argument is. Once again, we must choose. Either we are speaking of a divine intention, which we claim to know—in which case we have a right to think that it will

[1] A, 346. Cf. V, 238, n. 2.
[2] P, 233.

be realized (but if this is our choice we have to prove that there is a God, and also to examine very critically whatever knowledge we may think we have of his plans); or else we are studying cosmology. In the latter case it is arguable that the universe is tending in all directions at once, or, to take one possibility, in the direction which leads to more and more improbable assemblages; the coherence of the universe is in no way at stake if the natural functioning of its laws wipes out all spirit tomorrow. There is no failure, no miscarriage of plans, about it (assuming that these expressions mean anything); the laws of the cosmos lead to the results which inevitably flow from them and from the nature of things. These laws are not trying systematically to construct something which to us would be excellent. In many ways the result, up to the present, *is* excellent. But the coherence of the universe—and its coherence is certain—has nothing to do with any admiration that we may feel for the wonders of life. The coherence which we have reason to look for is still the same—as are, incidentally, all the treasures of the cosmos and its claim on our admiration—if life seems to come to a standstill, or evolution takes an unexpected turn.

Teilhard believes with all his heart and soul that even this does not say all that there is to be said; there is yet another form of coherence, over and beyond it. And it does indeed seem as if there were something like a plan which could be regarded as corresponding with the advance of the universe; some specific extra of intelligibility almost forces itself on the mind—not, it is true, as a certainty, but as a question that must not be left out of our study and research. Only, what we are considering is not a plan for the *cosmos*. Either we stick to hyperphysics, in which case I do not think the question can be dealt with as it should; or else we enter the realm of philosophy, and should—while never turning our backs on science—make use of entirely new methods.

If there is a design, it is *written in the cosmos,* and will therefore be revealed (or suggested) by scientific observation. And we must indeed take the cosmological study of evolution as our starting-point. Everything seems set for an ascent to spirit—and for an ascent of spirit towards even vaster achievements. By highly varied and complex means, nature goes forward, as it seems, unfalteringly, overcoming every difficulty, finding a way round every obstacle, and substituting a new process for any that has become obsolete. Is it merely by chance that earth has succeeded, with innumerable twists and turns of ingenuity, in first producing man, and then fostering his progress? How much clearer it would all be if the whole thing had been deliberately planned and arranged . . .

Only, we have to make our choice. Either there is a creative or controlling mind—a God, in other words—or there is no design, but only the deceptive appearance of one. We must, if we are to make up our minds between the two hypotheses, begin by looking into the question of the existence of God. To say that there is an aim in evolution is to say implicitly that there is a God; but without saying why.

Is Teilhard untouched by this criticism? He tries to found his reasoning on scientific observation, and on that alone. But he interprets evolutionary gravity as an advance towards consciousness, in which he sees *the* phenomenon, *the* law, the absolute direction of the advance of the cosmos. If this is so, he has indeed good grounds for believing that the advance will continue, true to its own past. Without bringing in any such thing as a deliberate aim or a divine plan, what he would have in mind is a cosmic force, a vector, which there would be no reason to suppose would become obsolete. But is there one single vector for evolution as a whole, and, if there is, may we take it that consciousness is really its aim? If, for example, it results, by its very nature, in improbable structures, all we can know is that it will go on producing other structures, even more improbable. But some accident may force it on to quite a different track; if human evolution comes to a halt, it

5+

will start off somewhere else. According to this theory, the universe does not irrevocably "personalize", it irrevocably "combines". Some contingency or other may put paid to a combination which today is flourishing. Disadvantageous mutations, ill-chosen selection, the triumph of brute or technical force over the true wisdom of the intelligence, an over-refinement which corrupts the mind (a phenomenon that may be caused by a biological transformation), and so on —not to mention the death of the species before maturation: if any of this lies ahead, the universe will still go on forming its combinations where it can. There is no guarantee whatever that evolution will stick to the line running from the primates to *homo sapiens*.[1]

Let us think of steel filings scattered over a sheet of cardboard: a magnetic field is then made by turning on electro-magnets, and fairly soon the filings form the regular lines of a spectrum. In observing this phenomenon, some spectator whose life-cycle was very short would have exactly the same impression that we have when we look at evolution. The process would seem to him an advance towards some aim. In

[1] There is another possibility—the end, which is no doubt near, of the syntropic wave. What is going to happen after that? A cosmic cataclysm, perhaps, followed by stagnation. In the approaching epoch shown by Cailleux's curves, mankind will not yet be properly unified.

reality there is no aim—only a physical force which moves gradually to the extreme limit of its result. What might chiefly interest the observer would be the decorative effect of the spectrum. But what he should look for, if he wanted to be objective, would be the *specific effect* of the physical force in question—the arrangement of the filings along the lines of the magnetic field.

This is a simple example, for there is only one factor at work—electro-magnetic force; whereas in evolution innumerable factors, both internal and external, come into play. Are these factors controlled by a systematic cause? This is by no means certain; and, if it were, what would the specific effect of this cause be? Moreover, if this cause does exist, it may not be—or may not always be—the dominant factor. The decisive part in the drama may pass from one factor to another, or from one group to another. The specific effect depends on which group of factors is the most important. And if consciousness is not produced as the specific effect, we cannot be sure that the future will go on perfecting it. Thus, what might, at the beginning of the proceedings, have seemed a very subtle distinction, now involves serious consequences. It is not all one whether the determining causes of evolution produce, directly, and as their specific effect, consciousness or improbable structures, or the highest possible degree of vital power.

If evolution is *in fact* an advance towards spirit, this may be due to a predisposition of things, organized by creative thought; but, unless we appeal to a divine intention, how can we be sure that cosmic functioning will always pursue the same effect; how are we to know that it is really incapable of going off at a tangent before it has completed what it (apparently) set out to do?

When Teilhard insists on the infallibility of evolution and the impossibility of its miscarriage, he has not, as I see it, furnished us with any proof. Yet we may think that evolution has a good chance of keeping to the same course. This is a likely opinion, and one that we may hang on to. But it does not authorize the conclusion that evolutionary progress will lead to a superorganism, or that the conditions necessary for the success of a superorganism will certainly be realized.

Let us, however, follow Père Teilhard de Chardin's reflections further. If the work of the universe is not to fail, what will be its requirements? This work is now chiefly entrusted to the psychological powers of man. Bearing as we do the responsibility of building up a planetary community and, in particular, a "communal thought", we ought to have the wish—no, we ought to have an all-absorbing longing—to advance along this line.

On his heaps of corn, coal, iron, uranium—
under whatever demographic pressure there
may be—the man of tomorrow will be on
strike if he ever loses his feeling for the ultra-
human. And not just an ordinary feeling, but
one that is deep and powerful, one that waxes
continually as his powers of vision and action
increase; one—to put it differently—capable of becoming paroxysmal, as that final
paroxysm, which he is called upon to make
ready, draws near.[1]

Now, as Teilhard sees it, the wish for evolutionary ascent is quite certainly doomed to come
to nothing, unless man may hope *to be for ever*;
unless the universe holds out to him the possibility of emerging, *whole and entire*, and with
all his achievements, from the general decay.
He will never make the heroic and continuous
efforts that his conquests demand, unless he
knows that these conquests are deathless. If man
is to continue his advance, quite objectively,
keeping step with the increase of his awareness,
then reality must be of such a nature that all
his wonderful hopes will not turn out to be
illusions.

This is the point which it seems to me essential to call to the notice, not of metaphysicians,
but of physicists, by insisting on the radical

[1] *A*, 232.

disactivation of energy which the expectation of total annihilation, or even of a diminished state, at the end of the phylogenesis now in progress, would entail for man.[1]

If thought is not to die out, there must be human survival, at least collective.[2] Here, in Teilhard's view, is the first point made. And, following on this: if the achievement is to have any solidity, the superorganism of the future must have a pre-existing centre. There is still discussion as to what constitutes the prerequisites for success. At one time, we heard a great deal about the psychological conditions that would be necessary if progress was to continue. Now the emphasis has shifted to defining the results to be achieved, and the ontological conditions that are implied, if evolutionary progress is ever to reach completion. The whole argument is based on one reading of the facts: evolution is a rise towards consciousness.

Therefore it should culminate forwards in some sort of supreme consciousness. But must not that consciousness, if it is to be supreme, contain in the highest degree what is the perfection of our consciousness—the illuminating involution of the being upon itself? It would manifestly be an error to extend the curve of hominization in the direction of a state of diffusion. It is only by hyper-reflection—that

[1] *A*, 360.   [2] *P*, 234.

is to say, hyper-personalization—that thought can extrapolate itself. Otherwise how could it garner our conquests which are all made in the field of what is reflected?[1]

This idea of a hyper-personalization, to which everything is leading up, first justifies the assertion that there will be a change of state transforming mankind from a society of persons into a new person, a soul of souls.[2] Then we see that such a structure would be too unsure, too precariously held together, if a personal centre were not already in existence, and all that had to be done was to unite with it. "Love . . . dies in contact with the impersonal and the anonymous."[3] The fusion of men into one single organism calls not only for progress of the intelligence but above all for an extraordinary broadening of our gift of sympathy. Teilhard thinks that this will come about through the affective attraction by which men will be drawn towards the Centre —but if the Centre is ideal or merely potential, such attraction will not be enough. Here we see again the preoccupation with the psychical factors that favour progress. The perfect completion of the work in hand seems so wholly beyond us as to be quite impossible: and yet it must infallibly come to pass (provided human freedom responds to the cosmic summons). This is only possible if there already exists a personal

[1] P, 258.   [2] P, 268.   [3] P, 269.

Centre, able to conquer men and bring them together. The attributes of this Centre are already defined—"autonomy, actuality, irreversibility, and thus finally transcendence".[1] Were it not for the pre-existence of Omega, there would be no real guarantee of success: we should not have the impetus to drive us forward: our soul would have the right to lie passive: reality would lack the evolutionary stimulus. Teilhard thinks that he has advanced some sort of proof of the existence of God—the "proof of complexity"[2] (the increase of complexity being equivalent to progress in personalization). Yet the wish to act and become unified "is entirely dependent on the conviction, strictly undemonstrable to science, that the universe has a direction and that it could—indeed, if we are faithful, it *should*—result in some sort of irreversible perfection. Hence comes belief in progress."[3] The "proof", then, rests on a belief that is "strictly undemonstrable to science".

I consider the evidence wholly unconvincing, because it in fact implies faith in the triumph of consciousness: and this, in the last resort, is equivalent to assuming the existence of God. It is simply begging the question to propound the hypothesis that the universe is advancing towards the highest possible degree of conscious-

[1] *P*, 271.
[2] "Vie et planètes", *Études*, May 1946, p. 166 *n*.
[3] *P*, 284.

ness, and that the requisite conditions for this cannot be lacking.[1]

At the very root of this argument, which I hold to be untenable, there lies no doubt a very wide-spread confusion, which is a temptation to all thinking men. The enquirer, who has his own ideas about reality (in this case, the tendency to see evolution as the growth of consciousness), quite simply identifies the reality with these ideas. He never stops to think that there is probably a discrepancy between a physical fact (complex, as such facts always are) and an idea in the mind, however true it may be. Reality is not to be identified with any intellectual blueprint, and agreement between the two can never be complete. Evolutionary progress *involves* a rise of psychisms, but it is not *identical* with an advance towards consciousness—consciousness as such; and thus it may not fulfil the demands of consciousness. Gnostic thought often succumbed to this sort of misapprehension—the misapprehension of believing a conceptual diagram to be interchangeable with reality. One then goes on to imagine, arguing from the diagram, that all the consequences one deduces from it will hold good of concrete things. The necessary stage of

[1] This postulate of Teilhard's has been compared with a scholastic principle—that a natural desire cannot be based on nothing. But this principle (the application of which is, in any case, terribly tricky) assumes—if it is to have any kind of validity—the existence of God.

5*

verification and criticism—which is much longer and more laborious than the stage of invention—is thus omitted.

I must make it quite clear that it would be doing Père Tielhard de Chardin a grave injustice to regard him as a gnostic. His religious speculations, in particular, are of a wholly different type from those of the various gnoses, and incomparably more valuable; and, although his mind is, up to a point, in harmony with Oriental thought (which, on the whole, is a very good thing), he yet disciplines these influences, and thereby completely transforms them, by his sense of the incarnation of the spiritual, and his sense of personalization. It is in the field of philosophical reflection that Teilhard disconcertingly yields to a temptation whose most striking examples we see in gnosis (but also in some of the scholastics, in Spinoza and Hegel and others who did not sufficiently exorcise the spirit of system).

Teilhard wanted to develop scientific reflection, but what he did was to overstep the boundaries of science and the philosophy of the sciences (hyperphysics). He overstepped them either by using arguments unacceptable to science, or by entering a province where the writ of science no longer runs.[1] His mistake lay in not seeing that, past a certain point, one

[1] His ideas on planetization, on the superorganism which is Somebody, are probably not outside the pro-

has to change one's discipline, for the type of
problem is completely different, and calls for
quite a different method.

To avoid over-subtlety, let us confine ourselves to two levels of reflection:

That of science, carried over into hyperphysics, in which our whole concern is to learn
as much as we can about phenomena.

That of philosophy in the true sense of the
word—philosophy as dealing with ontological
problems, and, here in particular, with problems
raised by the fact that things have a meaning for
the spirit.

As far back as Socrates,[1] it was seen quite
clearly that there has to be a complete change
of method when one passes from the first level
to the second. I hold that this necessity becomes
increasingly urgent as the practice of thought
continues. We must not delude ourselves into
thinking that a single movement of the mind,
with science as its starting-point, will lead us to
those supreme truths that we are seeking. It may

---

vince of hyperphysics, although they are at the extreme
edge of it. The concept of the human prolongation of
evolution is derived from science in its wider sense. It
is only the method of reflection which is unscientific,
because it is not sufficiently objective. As soon as we
touch on the problems of God and survival (even
collective survival) we are entering on metaphysical
exigencies—even if we approach them from the physical
side.

[1] According to Plato. See the *Phaedo,*

be hoped that philosophy will not ignore the claims of science and will remain as far as possible in touch with it; but, since philosophy is dealing with problems of quite a different type, it calls for an altogether new form of mental training, and a clear recognition of what its methods should be.

An impression that we have already felt comes over us more strongly than ever: Teilhard's argument in reality assumes both the existence of God, and the author's own knowledge of the plans of creation. If we grant this, his inference has some meaning; if God wills spirit, he will have it, and completely. So long as we really know what we are about, this kind of reflection may be of great interest. The proposed line of reasoning then constitutes, in philosophy, the second stage of reflective thinking which has already established the existence of God. It henceforth confines itself to predicting the collective personality of mankind in the future, its survival, and its union with God.

Even put thus, the inference is, I think, open to question. Supposing God only wanted to bring into being a certain number of men, give them consciousness and leave them to get on with it, then wipe out the whole attempt and start afresh on something else? Or again, supposing he intends to complete evolution on some other planet and let it run to seed, so to speak, on this one? We could not say that the designs of God were incoherent in either of these hypothetical cases. When it comes to the question of God and his intentions, we can only state what is, and then perhaps take it upon ourselves, at our own risk, to put our own interpretation on the facts; but it is certainly not for us to lay down a course of action that God *must* follow if he does not intend to abandon his own plan. We simply do not know whether God wants the highest possible degree of consciousness, or whether collective consciousness would have to be centred like a person.

Man lets himself in for some terrible shocks when he tries to fathom the designs of God. This is not the place to discuss the problem of evil, which calls for exhaustive treatment and deserves a book to itself. But it is this problem that underlies the question under discussion. We always rush to the conclusion that God cannot possibly commit some act or other which lets down our ideal; and yet this is just what happens. Then we hunt round to see if we can find some way out by which, after all, what he did *was* justified, although in some other way; and we are reduced to guesswork. But we keep coming back to the words of Isaias: "Your thoughts are not my thoughts, nor your ways my ways."[1]

[1] Isa. 55.8.

In metaphysics as in hyperphysics, Teilhard's views on the meeting of mankind with Omega rest on a hypothesis. Yet one point remains: is there any guarantee for such concepts in Christian belief—any guarantee that would authorize Christians, in the name of their religious convictions, to regard them as more or less certain, or as based on theology? If Teilhard has really brought Christian doctrine face to face with scientific thought, if he has succeeded in forming these two visions of the world into a synthesis, he has done something of major importance. We must examine his concept from this angle.

NOTE. How is the philosophical problem to be treated? I have already said that a new method should have been adopted—a method that was neither that of science nor of Teilhard de Chardin. I may, then, indicate in a few words the form that this new method might take. I will only deal with it briefly, although the problem is one that calls for very thorough treatment. There is a technique of philosophy, just as there is a technique of science; and it is no less difficult: but this is not the place to undertake it, for we can allow ourselves no more than a glance at the subject.

What we have to consider is the fact that evolution, seen by the human spirit, is something with a meaning. We must, of course, allow only to have any weight with us such significances as are certain; such significances as—the nature of spirit being

what it is—are ineluctible. Once this has been established, the fact that phenomena have a high degree
of significance raises a specific problem; and the first
thing we must do is to see what it is, and wherein
it differs from the problems set by science.

To do this, we may take one of Teilhard's own
assertions as our starting-point. The human spirit,
he tells us, prolongs, although by another process,
the main line of biological evolution—the line
which produces the most striking psychical results.
We might, perhaps, start off on firmer ground, for
the statement is not absolutely incontestable; but
we shall come across other significant factors—the
most certain.

If henceforth the advance of consciousness is to
make use, above all, of the unification of mankind
and collective work, having begun by the morphological modification of the individual, and in particular the construction of the brain—if all this is
so, the process of evolution is undergoing a change.
And this change of technique takes place just at the
moment when it becomes necessary, if the significance of the results so far achieved is to be increased.
The possible explanations are as follows:

It is all due to chance.

It can all be explained by a systematic cause
within the cosmic order.

We must look for an explanation of another
order. A probable one is this: the universe is the
instrument of a Mind—a Mind which has combined physical causes in such a way as to work out
an all-embracing design.

The most alluring hypothesis is that which
neither rests content with mere chance nor falls

back upon some transcendental Mind. An explanation of this sort would not run into any theoretical difficulties if we could be sure that the *same physical cause* lay behind the first stages of evolution and the law which is now urging human beings to unite. Then we should understand the continuity of a result which progresses in a regular manner: consciousness is continually on the increase, because it is a result (direct or indirect) of a cause that is ceaselessly at work. The change of process raises no special problem if both the old process and the new derive from one general cause. But no mutations, no selection, no, not even that small admixture of Lamarckism that we should, no doubt, retain—not all these put together can explain the tendency of men to form into groups and thereby increase the phenomenon of consciousness. The causes which, up to the appearance of man, brought about evolution, have now more or less reached their limit, for it is no longer through them that the advance of consciousness continues. Unless we put the whole thing down to some lucky chance, what is in fact the force which, just at the right moment, replaces an obsolete process by one that is new and better? And this force must be able to control both animal evolution and the spiritual destiny of the human community.

As far as the explanation of this problem is concerned, Meyer's hypothesis carries quite exceptional weight. Let us suppose that this theory, or one like it, is sufficiently worked out, and that science has adopted it. The universe is so made that it should bring about ever fuller and more complex assemblages. Morphological evolution has culminated in that improbable structure, the human brain. Whether or not the human individual can be brought to a still higher state of perfection, the universe, acting by its own law of combination, goes on blindly working out all possible arrangements, especially in the social sphere. Men are thus drawn to group themselves together—urged, no doubt, by some physical phenomenon which has its repercussions at the psychical level. We can understand that cultural collaboration should lead to an increase of consciousness; this result is in fact obtained by a universe which had no such thing in mind. Above all the changing processes, there is indeed a systematic cause which ensures continual progress; it increases complexity, of which consciousness is only the repercussion.

Is this explanation wholly satisfactory, even if we accept it as being scientifically impregnable? As regards its bearing on the particular problem we are concerned with—the problem, that is to say, of the continued progress of consciousness, despite all changes of process—it makes for an element of intelligibility which is impressive enough. Yet, even here, there is one disturbing feature. Not every combination leads to psychism; some of our machines are more improbable than the lower animals, yet have not their instinct. Life produces a very special type of assemblages—those, precisely, which go with psychism. When we have to explain the fact that one process, capable of increasing consciousness, and probably now exhausted, is replaced by another, equally able to carry consciousness a stage further—when we want to explain all this, we fall back on chance. We have a material explanation; and that, on the purely scientific level, is enough. We then add: *It so happens* that the new phenomenon which produces combinations also produces consciousness.

Moreover, the syntropic wave will have to produce minds and collective mental realities, as it has already produced vegetable and animal life. We must face the problem squarely and explain how the physical process of "advanced" actions can lead to the fusion of minds and their mutual enrichment. Is it really still a matter of material combinations, only more improbable than any that has gone before? Either there is a spiritual cause, quite distinct from "advanced" actions, or else the whole thing is to be explained by material dispositions (which determine the life of the spirit). If the latter explanation is true, the continued advance of consciousness is just a bit of luck.

The fact that, at a given moment, one process takes over from another, is not the only problem with which the philosopher is faced. Taken by itself, it would be of little weight; but it is part of an immense whole. Everything in life rises up to the realization of spirit. This world-wide fact is so profoundly significant that any attempt to explain it by chance seems absurd. It is incomparably more intelligible that such a result should have a specific cause. Any study of the subject that goes into it at all deeply should, of course, at this point consider the rival theory that the world is absurd, and debate the question of whether a theory which is far more intelligible is necessarily more true. It would have to be shown that, where biological data are concerned, the meaning or significance of the

phenomena lies to a great extent in the facts themselves, and not in the human consciousness that
observes them. It is this accumulation of meanings,
bursting forth in innumerable ingenuities as in the
movement of the whole, which sets the philosopher
a problem. With this problem—the problem of ex-
plaining *meaning* as such—science, strictly speaking, has nothing to do; its one concern is to take
due note of the *existence* of the phenomena.
Voltaire insisted that there must be a clock-maker
to explain the clock; the remark makes a scientist
smile, for he knows very well that the highly perfected clock with which the group of living things
is compared, was constructed by the cosmos; or,
alternatively, the cosmos is a clock that is making
itself, bit by bit. This means that, *once we have
accepted the existence of the universe with its laws*,
the existence of the clock does not call for any
craftsman other than the cosmos itself. But, when a
philosopher thinks of a clock-maker, he does not
think of him as *making* the clock (the universe does
that), but as *thinking* it. The universe with its laws
is perhaps already impregnated with thought—that
is to say, fashioned by it: which is why it leads to
results of the same nature as thought. Whatever it
may be, the nature of the mechanism producing
these results—the one thing that science is concerned with—does not affect the decisive fact; the
results have meaning. Doubtless the phenomena
often take us aback; they are not what we should
have expected: but (to transpose slightly Bergson's
saying about the *order* of reality) their apparent non-
sense is a sense that we do not like. In any event, we
are left with a considerable sum-total of meaning,

and we have no difficulty in imagining that it might be infinitely less (we have only to think of the universe before there was any life). The world shows signs of so much meaning that we try to find an explanation of it. A new sector of intelligibility thereby opens to us. It will remain a void until we can find some cause of all this meaning which is a specific cause, and not purely fortuitous. A very simple illustration will show how this is to be understood. If two stars collide, the trajectory of each has its own specific cause, but the collision of the two has not; it is due to the meeting of two independent causal series. Where a very large number of phenomena appear to have no specific cause, precisely as regards that aspect which gives them their meaning, we begin to wonder if we have not overlooked the principal thing. Even when the scientific explanation is complete (the trajectory of each star established, and the mechanism of the biological phenomena), the philosophical problem still remains unsolved.

Does not science itself provide the material for this new explanation? This is a question that has to be examined in detail. All anti-chances (polarized light, the possible cause of the first asymmetrical structures, selection, any Lamarckian factors that there may be, and, possibly, the syntropic wave) are *partial* specific causes, which go some way to accounting for all the significances, but cannot do so entirely. They explain how the organization of matter takes place; and organization itself is meaning to spirit. But the organizations that have in fact been achieved are not just haphazard; in many cases they look, in detail, like the solution of some problem; and, taken as a whole, they lead to the mind of man. When we explain meaning as the effect of anti-chances, we are supposing the arrangement of the universe and of physical laws to be such as to result in the convergence that we observe; the "planned" advance of the universe no longer astounds us, for it is the result of physical causes; the really astonishing part of it all is the fundamental data—the ordering of the universe with its laws. We have not, then, found a specific cause of the meaning of things so long as we continue to base this meaning once for all on a "miraculous" (although fortuitous) organization at the level of the fundamental data. I have here done no more than summarize what should be the points of a far longer study—a study which would show the significant aspect of biological phenomena to be in part unexplained (unexplained fundamentally), so long as we looked no further than cosmic causes. Such a work would have to be completed by observation of human spiritual phenomena, for here too there is the same necessity for making the significances intelligible.

Finally, we may find explanations which, however perfect they may be on the scientific level, look flimsy enough when applied to those problems of origin which never cease to haunt the philosophic mind. In this respect, such explanations are wholly inadequate.

Even a systematization such as Meyer's cannot assign a specific cause for the ascent to spirit; all it does is to account for the fact of assemblage. But we can understand the advance towards spirit if the universe is organized by a creative Thought.

This suggestion, however, does not solve everything; it deals less with the problem than with its opposite. Any really stringent philosophical procedure will require the minimum hypothesis—or rather, the hypothesis that best agrees with the facts: what is the condition adequate to explain the phenomenon of spirit? There is a striking, and perhaps perfect, answer to this question in Heidegger's concept of Being: the given must be or contain a light which renders things intelligible and the mind penetrable to their meaning (man is the "guardian" or "shepherd" of being in its truth or manifestation). The "Being" of Heidegger is neither God nor the ground of the world, but a radiance of intelligibility, the nature of which is, moreover, very mysterious. Being lays on man a sort of mission: it bids him understand and put into words a fact that is as yet hidden. We sometimes catch an echo of Heidegger in Teilhard de Chardin when he tells us (*A*, 341: cf. *V*, 378) that the play of evolutionary forces *summons* us, *destines* us (to the heights of hominization).

Stated thus, the problem involves another: What structure of reality is necessitated by Being? Does it imply the existence of God? This is a very difficult question; we have to discover how being is related to a subject, or subjects, of existence, and what this (or these) must be, if being is not to be inferior to what we know of it. Here I merely wanted to point out that reflection on biological and human problems leads logically to this final question.

8

ON THE POSITIVE SIDE

B EFORE we go any further, let us take a general look round to see how much, of the theories already mentioned, we may safely accept. We have gone into them for the express purpose of determining the true nature of the problems and the degree of certainty attained. It has been, as it were, a filtering process, and we now have to consider the residue left to us. And, undoubtedly, we find ourselves with a number of ideas which are new enough and of value to us today. The sum total of conclusions is such as to show, if not unanimity (that is out of the question), at least a wide range of agreement between very different types of mind.

Those who condemn Teilhard de Chardin have never seen what it is in him that makes him so attractive, nor the reasons justifying one's final capitulation to him. He felt, very deeply, certain intellectual and spiritual needs of our time. The solutions he proposes, imperfect though they may be, are already such as can be used; at times they are excellent, if regarded simply as suggestions. It is for us to carry the work a stage further.

We are, in the first place, invited to search natural history, and the history of mankind, for any indications of the *function* of man. As we read Teilhard, we see more clearly how man ought to live if he is to function aright. Henri Poincaré said very truly that science is in the indicative and morality in the imperative; but he was wrong in thinking that all science was therefore powerless in moral matters. The imperative is prompted, or at least called for, by that which is. When a doctor makes a diagnosis, the treatment to be followed depends on the data (in the indicative), these data being the normal state of the organism, and the nature of its disturbance. In the same way, in morality, it is not just a question of cherishing some sort of utopian idealism, however lofty or noble, but of living according to what we are; for what we are determines what we should be. This incontrovertible idea may be regarded as one of the universal discoveries of our day.

And to know what is, we have to start off from physics, with the added dimension given it by hyperphysics. The whole of wisdom is not to be found in science, even seen in this light; but neither the philosopher nor the man of religious mind can afford to shut his eyes to the truths that science has revealed.

One of these truths is evolution. It is impossible to form a true understanding of the nature of the human being unless we see him as part of a historical series, standing between past and future. Nothing, certainly, is more important for us to understand than the function of spirit. Let us, then, try to consider the relation between spirit and evolution, or, alternatively, between spirit and life.

We may take it as proved that spirit itself has a history bound up with the evolution of life as a whole.[1] Many facts in contemporary history become more intelligible if we see them as so many advances on the Middle Ages (or the nineteenth century), and as fumbling attempts to find still more highly evolved formulae. Not only must we accept, in good time, the inevitable changes and renewals, if we are not to waste them and so pile up difficulties for ourselves: but it is inherent in our nature to turn towards the future, and all we do will be more or less barren if we refuse to recognize this necessity.

We do not know *how* spirit is dependent on the forces of evolution, and we do not need to know. These forces are hard to analyse, and we may even wonder whether they will not henceforth be lacking. But because they are multiple,

[1] The graphs of Cailleux and Meyer, which have already been mentioned, provide convincing evidence of this. I have also accepted part of Teilhard's own argument (see pp. 101–3, 105–6).

because one factor can take over from others before being obliterated in its turn, it seems likely that not all is lost, and that man may yet hope in the promise of still greater life. Let us, however, follow the less encouraging hypothesis through to the end. Let us suppose that mankind will no longer have the cosmos to help it and will be forced to rely only on itself; even so, it will still have the resources of its own powers to draw on. The study of evolution and the human species, as Teilhard knew it (we must discount his exaggerations), shows the direction in which, through our efforts, our life may advance. By perfecting both our own powers of consciousness (lucidity, freedom) and our social unification, we shall be continuing the line along which life has achieved success.

Here, it seems to me, is ground on which all can take their stand. There are some who will raise this ideal still higher by religious spirituality. Those who remain outside any religious movement will still be able, by fulfilling, to the utmost, the mission of spirit, to build up not only an excellent temporal achievement but something that is itself a form of spiritual life.

The vocation of spirit—a vocation that has become visible, concrete, a thing of absorbing interest: this is the discovery that we owe to Teilhard's thought. We can make what applications of it we will, and it is to be hoped that they will be made with great conscientiousness; in any case, a line of enquiry has been shown us, which it would be a thousand pities not to follow through.

We must not shut our eyes to the obvious objection. It is possible that spirit and life are in irreconcilable opposition, and that excess of life stifles spirit. This way of looking at it is plausible enough, and has moreover some tradition behind it. And, on the other hand, if such an opinion is not based on the nature of things, we run the risk of falling into Nietzsche's extremes. If natural history authorizes us to see the development of spirit as merely the prolongation of life, there will no longer be any principles, any morality, any disinterestedness, any depth— nothing but the triumphant explosion of life at its strongest and most reckless. In both of these cases, as the natural curve of life mounts, spirit goes astray.

I shall not try to meet these objections with a decisive answer that would put them out of court; on the contrary, I think that they should both remain as permanently open questions— warnings of the inevitable dangers. Our progress would thus be considerably more assured.

I think, indeed, that between life and spirit there is a secret—limited—opposition, as well as relative continuity. The transition to a higher level, the change of state of which Teilhard speaks (the "threshold of reflection"), explains this twofold aspect.

Biologically speaking, it is likely enough that the forces of evolution do favour the stronger life, regardless of its quality; this is certainly so, if selection is the dominant factor; it is then the vocation of spirit to resist the invitation of cosmogenesis. If we are keenly alive to the general upward trend of evolution, and the persuasive powers emanating from it, we shall be tempted to use our spirit in the cause of greater force, rather than of truth and justice.

Let us reason for a moment within this hypothesis. Should we then have to oppose Teilhard's thesis? Not exactly, for if spirit is true to its nature as spirit—if it is aware of its higher status, and of the change of state which has made it what it is—it can make use of cosmic forces even while it amends them, bending them into the service of its own ideal. Whether spirit is of a nature that transcends matter, or simply a property of the stuff of matter (a characteristic property of matter rightly organized), the conclusion is still the same; spirit has the power to draw back from the impulsions of nature.[1]

We should be wrong in thinking that cosmic forces, so long as we hearkened to their undistorted echoes within us, would lead us automatically to God. It is we who give them their human and moral undertones. Thus, in our day, the upward trend of evolution certainly

[1] We see here the predominant idea in Vercors' novel, *Les Animaux dangereux.*

leads to the growth of industrialization. It would be idle to try to halt this movement, which corresponds to a sort of biological necessity. But its human consequences depend on our freedom —whether they are to be peace or war, social justice or exploitation, cultural refinement (especially in the use of leisure) or the pursuit of trivial pleasures, a greater virility as a result of our new tasks, or a sort of fatty degeneration brought on by comfort—to name only some of the possibilities. The forces of evolution are neither moral nor immoral, and their consequences (industrialization among them) can be turned either way; it is man who uses them, for or against the natural ends of spirit.

That there is here a temptation is undeniable. If spirit allows the impulsion of evolution to have its own way, if it fails to choose the direction along which this impetus will take it, it will run into disaster. The temptation is, moreover, legion; which is why the details of its mechanism do not greatly matter. There may, indeed, be some fear of spirit's shaking off its ties with universal life, and, by losing its contact with nature, losing all wisdom too. (It was this possibility that worried Klages.) On the other hand, spirit may fall into the clutches of vital forces, become their slave, and thus suffer the worst estrangement of all; would it not be better to hold back a bit—not to yield entirely to cosmic pressure? And if spirit is intoxicated by life (as in Nietzsche's concept), it runs the risk, in this heady state, of losing all its most precious qualities—modesty, deep humanity, disinterested love, complete objectivity.[1]

It is true that spirit is a higher form of life. But the ways of cosmic life, if we retain them more or less as they are, may well be injurious to spiritual justice and uprightness. The cosmic drive must be used, as a positive force, but the movements of instinct have to be controlled; otherwise, spirit may perhaps be strong, but it will be hard, and some of its functions (and these the most delicate and subtle) will suffer from a kind of sclerosis. We can best appreciate the true function of spirit by considering *what spirit is*, and not merely by examining its biological antecedents (which are more apparent and more certain than its future). The study of its powers, aspirations, revulsions and present experiences is more enlightening than the study of the evolutionary process. Two trends, objec-

[1] Nietzsche was not indifferent to these qualities. The true Nietzsche, as his letters in particular showed him to be, is strangely different from the picture one ordinarily has of him. The disadvantages of a Nietzschean outlook on the world should not be treated sketchily, and the brief mention here made of it should, by rights, be amplified and the finer shades of his thought brought out. But this is not the subject under discussion, and all I want, by my allusion to Nietzsche, is to point out that a problem does exist.

tively speaking very different, seem possible: spirit-life, or spirit-spirit.

In the first trend—the trend of spirit-life—it is the most creative psychical powers that are brought into play—the powers that sway ideas and people, that bring in vast changes, that make for full and highly coloured lives—for Leonardo da Vinci, Goethe, Paul Valéry... Clemenceau, Sacha Guitry, Citroën. Spirit, seen in the light of the second concept, seeks the values of contemplation, disinterestedness, the higher forms of love, the contact of the intelligence with the deepest realities—Plato, St. Augustine, St. Thomas Aquinas, Gandhi. A successful synthesis of the two is extremely rare (Aristotle? St. Francis of Assisi?). But this synthesis should obviously be attempted. Each of the two types degenerates if it is too remote from the other, Teilhard saw that they ought to be united, and he tried to unite them. To sever these two fundamental trends, as the world of today might be tempted to do, would lead to disaster.

For this reason among others, it is absolutely essential for East and West to draw together. The traditional East has an immense aptitude for seeking out those developments that are most spiritual. We are in danger of misunderstanding such developments (as the East is of losing them), because the East never knew our need for widespread technological construction

and material goods. Teilhard helps us to unite
the two worlds, not only by upholding the ideal
of the total unification of mankind, but by his
own example and tendencies.

The consideration of the All; the spiritual life
lived in relation to the cosmos (although purified
by strict detachment): care to hear the voice of
matter in a deeply religious spirit; indifference
to ontological structures—all these are Eastern
characteristics, and they are all to be found in
Teilhard. Instead of analysing things rationally,
Eastern thought—and Teilhard's too—awakens
the soul. A music is played for us, and we must
learn how to listen. Then we rise up and live—
in harmony. We have felt a breath of air, and
come out of a prison whose atmosphere was
stifling us.

The interest in science, industry, action, the
meaning of evolution—all these are Western
preoccupations. The great problem today is undoubtedly that of finding some way of taking
science in one's stride and going beyond it, yet
without falling into purely subjective considerations. Even if Teilhard's method did not quite
achieve all that it set out to do, he was at least
making an attempt which it is imperative for
us to take over from him and carry further.
Through him, a new suggestion has been put to
us, an invitation to an intellectual and spiritual
life at once strong and sensitive.

Teilhard had a very personal sense of the

bonds uniting spirit to the cosmos, but for all
that he did not deny the difficulties that spirit
will have to overcome if it is to be at home in
the universe, and yet not suffer any diminution
from its immersion in space and time. Whatever
Camus may say, man is not a stranger to the
world or to social life; there, indeed, are his
roots. None the less, spirit is to some extent out
of its element when it becomes conscious of
itself; it feels to some degree a stranger on earth,
for all its ties. This comes, no doubt, from the
effort it has to make in order to confer the
addition of new meaning on physical realities.[1]
To make these truly human (to give, for instance, the raw facts of evolution their final significance), spirit must not be borne along on the
cosmic current; it must draw from its own
depths. Otherwise it is not doing its work. But
a man who honestly gives himself up to the
action of spirit, and exercises it at all fully, will
find (if his mental vision is clear) that he is in
fact in harmony with nature. I understand Teilhard's thought in this sense, and endorse it; man

[1] I have already said that natural biological data
necessarily contain a considerable amount of meaning
(ch. 7, pp. 139–40) and also that they can be made either
moral or immoral by the additional meaning imposed
on them (pp. 148–50). These two assertions can be
upheld simultaneously. By taking possession of the
data, and integrating them into his own universe, man
gives them a new meaning—a meaning which may to
some extent contradict the first.

6+

is not at war with the cosmos, nor is he an exile therein: he finds in it what he needs for even the highest functions of spirit. Spirit can create meaning, even while cleaving to the natural structures; indeed, this is how it best does so; each operation reinforces the other. Although Plato did not think so, no violence was done to the normal condition of spirit by setting it in the universe. This would have been the view of Thomas Aquinas, although perhaps he would have urged that there still remained a certain divergence—irreducible, however slight—between spirit and earth. Would Teilhard have accepted this distinction? Possibly; in any case, he quite understood that man has to put himself above nature, not merge into it. The strictures on Rousseau's "naturism" do not apply to Teilhard.

If we are to continue his line of thought, we must, I think, ask ourselves whether spirit as a whole is in full harmony with the cosmos from which it sprang. Even Nietzsche, who saw consciousness as existing to serve the will to power, yet thought that the unconditional will to know tended in the opposite direction (and should be retained).[1] Or perhaps the will to power (that

[1] In Nietzsche's thought as a whole, the quest for truth is given a very high place (although it should be transcended in a larger truth, beyond the intellect).
The will to power, which is the basic reality, is nature's means of advance towards more life, which

is to say, the secret tendency of nature) only attains its full dimensions when, having reached the plane of spirit, it gives up the struggle in so far as it relates to domination, and thinks mainly of love. Were this to happen, only a narrow interpretation of the promptings of the cosmos would run counter to the vocation of spirit. The "Yes" to life would cover everything.

In the concrete, it seems as if there is always some resistance or other to overcome. And, so long as there are men on earth, they will have to reflect on the relationship between the spirit and cosmos—and do so, not merely in a theoretical manner, but observing the results of their own various courses of action.

All men are made, by the nature of their situation, to collaborate in a common task. Here, perhaps, is the central idea of the whole argument—the idea which most lends itself to practical application. It would be difficult to deny its truth, even though one might not connect it quite as closely as does Teilhard with the trend of the forces of evolution. It is true that points of detail are still in doubt in many technical

_____

culminates in poetic ecstasy or the creative "explosion" of a musical composer. The tendency (or "will") to this type of power is seen as a characteristic of fundamental being. Up to a point, this idea forecasts Teilhard's. There is even, in Nietzsche, something like a form of pan-psychism.

discussions; does the force of evolution, for instance, keep pace with selection—is it a struggle
rather than a collaboration? Is the universe still
contracting?—and so on. But we are left with
at least one certainty; *because we have reached
the stage of spirit*, we must learn to know one
another and to work together. (Moreover, the
theory of a contracting universe, although it
raises a great many difficult questions, really
seems to have a certain value at the present day;
human history is in a line of relative continuity
with evolution.) Any temptation to individual-
ism that might beset us is rebutted by Teilhard
in a very interesting way, on strictly biological
grounds, based on observation of the human
species, and, for this reason, valid, whatever may
be the truth about the forces of evolution. It
has been thought that civilization would culminate in separate persons; mankind would be
like a mountain range, made up of a great many
foothills—the mediocrities—and a few peaks.
But there is an ascent, an upward thrust, of the
whole, or the peaks would not be what they are;
it is as well for these human peaks not to cut
themselves off from the community and its line
of enquiry. Elementary laws oblige us to draw
together; the growing population squeezes us
closer and closer on the restricted surface of the
planet; economic and technical organization
both call for union.[1] But there is much more in

[1] G, 130, 131.

it than that; the unity that can be established
between men fosters interiority and freedom.[1]
Even at the lower biological stages, there is more
life at the level of the species than at that of
the individual. The total capacities of any given
organic form only appear with the complete
species; the individual has no great share in
them. This law holds good, of course, of mankind, and thus the individual stands to gain,
if he can, from the life of the whole species.
Now, as a result of human psychism, this total
sharing does in fact become possible among men,
whereas, among animals, it is slight enough.
Through travel, the press and wireless we can
be in touch with the work and discoveries of
the whole world. More than this, even; the life
of the species, as such, can, in the case of man,
expand and develop in an amazing way. Collective work, if it is well organized, greatly increases
the potentialities of the human brain; the work
of research not only calls for the stimulation and
enrichment of mind by mind, but for a pooling
of material resources; laboratory experiments
today need the help of heavy industry. Intellectual work itself, then, should be organized on
a world-wide scale. But shall we have the genius,
when research has become far more collective
than it is now, to keep alight the flame of individual freedom and imagination? It should be
quite possible, in spite of all the obstacles.

[1] G, 132, 133.

The danger would lie in our neglecting the spiritual perfection of the individual. Up to now, culture, in the best meaning of the word, has been the product of intensive effort—an effort that called for life-long perseverance and a degree of heroic detachment bordering on self-isolation. Great intellectuals, like the great figures in religious life, carried their heavy burdens almost alone. Are we to think that the ease and enthusiasm of communal work can take the place of this solitary toil? We should then be choosing a wholly new mode of life, one with nothing in common with its predecessor—a life in which humanity advanced as one, with its greatest men striving to build up a civilization rather than themselves—and with the austerity that was once needed melting away as if by magic. This would be a very serious mistake. Certain forms of austerity may disappear or diminish, but the fundamental demands of the situation will not be any the less. I think it is true that we have to aim more at a collective ideal. Only, if there is to be no explicit quest for individual perfection; if the whole effort goes into building up an economic and social structure; industry may perhaps make strides, but our humanity will not be much further forward.

What are we to build on, in our attempt to bring about some first beginning of planetary union? According to Maritain, nothing could be more idle than to try to unite men on some least common denominator of philosophy.

However small, however modest, however tentative this may be, it will perpetually give rise to contests and divisions. And this quest of a common denominator in contrasting convictions can develop nothing but intellectual cowardice and mediocrity, a weakening of minds and a betrayal of the rights of truth.[1]

Pluralist society will, then, find its source of unity not in any profession of faith but in human friendship, shot through, as Maritain hopes, with the influences of Christianity. This is not so very different from Père Teilhard de Chardin's view, although the two approaches are not, perhaps, identical. Teilhard also accepts plurality of opinions; he even believes that all enquiry helps on the general progress; and his hopes are centred in the construction of collective work (which is something very like the union of friendship). But apparently he does believe in a doctrinal minimum that should be common to all; he believes in the general acceptance of science and its consequences.

It is, indeed, likely enough that science will become increasingly the basis on which everything, everywhere, is built, however much the various theories may differ in detail. Will this

[1] *True Humanism*, Bles, 1938, p. 167.

be enough to ensure temporal wisdom? By no means. Many scientists, who pay tribute to Père Teilhard de Chardin's technical competence and who, as far as palaeontology goes, are in agreement with him, yet find a very different interpretation for the general results; and the human significance that they see in them is wholly other. Those matters on which science can pronounce with certainty do not solve the great problems of humanity, over which every man alive has his own ideas; there can be, and are, widely different views of man's destiny, the question of which virtues it is most important to acquire, and even of the life of the mind. It is true that the "human" sciences, psychology in particular, will one day give us knowledge that we can trust completely. But there will always be different philosophies, *mystiques* at variance with one another, religions and those who oppose them. And there will always be that fundamental division of which I have already spoken —the division between spirit-life and spirit-spirit.

Is it possible to find any great objective data, midway between the technique of the sciences and the views of philosophy and religion? The hope that Teilhard has inspired in us is that of a wellnigh universal agreement, to be reached on such grounds as these. And, as I see it, Teilhard succeeded, to some extent, in this attempt.

Life has in fact risen towards organization, towards greater psychic powers, towards lucidity and freedom; no one wants to run counter to this movement; everyone wants, if possible, to prolong it; and undoubtedly we can all work at unifying the world and bringing the sciences to a higher pitch of perfection. We can also learn, gradually, by helping each other, and making use even of the differences between us, to come to a right understanding of science with its methods and results (and also its limitations). There is important work to be done here, and probably no one is as yet fully up to it. Here, then, beyond the frontiers of science, is a firm foundation for all alike, a foundation whose first stones are already laid, and on which a great deal can be built (especially along the lines of psychology, sociology and the other human branches of science). We owe Teilhard a debt for having pointed it out to us. He is at one, over all this, with other men of good will in our own day—such men as Saint-Exupéry, for instance. He has stronger, more precise arguments than they in support of the same ideal—although even his are not quite as clinching as we should like.

But his outlook scans yet another horizon. He holds that the Christian way of life is peculiarly in harmony with the cosmic reality. He thinks that, by unifying the earth, mankind will be

6*

doing the work of Christ; and he tries to explain why this is so. It now remains for us to look at this aspect of his thought—the most fascinating and the most hotly disputed of all.

PART 3

THEOLOGY

9

THE QUESTIONS OF CHRISTIANS:
THE FINAL PLEROMA

THOSE of Teilhard's readers who are Christians often have mixed feelings over him. They see in him a spiritual radiance of a very personal kind, whose innermost essence seems admirable. But they cannot help wondering whether, in his concept of Christianity, there are not hidden weaknesses which will only come to light after some considerable time.

I too have gone through such moments of doubt, and have come to the conclusion, after long reflection, that there is nothing in them.[1] Teilhard's thought does, indeed, need to be *completed* on several important points; it must, for instance, be made quite clear that there must be no compromise about the absolute "otherness" of the supernatural order; that there are some values which evolution does not bring into being, and conflicts which may set them in opposition to the actual movements of nature;

[1] I can, of course, only express my personal feeling in the matter. But I shall try to confront Teilhard with Catholic teaching as it is.

but there is nothing to prevent us from formulating these complementary considerations, and they do not give the lie to Teilhard's work. There are, moreover, certain additional distinctions to be made; indispensable clarifications are lacking in the text; but these essential explanations do not undermine the priest's thought. His language is at times ambiguous, some of his formulae are unfortunate, and his ideas are not always sufficiently worked out. These gaps are regrettable; yet behind this disappointing exterior we can see very acute intuitions—intuitions that give rise to many others and may well infuse new blood into Christian thought.

The subject of evolution should not, in itself, cause any difficulties. Teilhard had a neat phrase for it—"God makes things make themselves"— gradually, in accordance with their laws. God, to St. Thomas, was the First Cause, not a secondary cause; in other words, the Creator is not just one cause among others; he is the foundation of all causes, and science can never discover him. The scientific explanation finds completion without once leaving the plane of secondary causes and their natural activity. From the point of view of creation, there is no stumbling-block in man's being the culmination of a material, animal evolution. If science claimed to rule out all ontological discontinuity, the only thing to be challenged would be the Catholic belief in the transcendence of the human soul over matter; but, as Teilhard repeatedly pointed out, the continuity in which science believes is the continuity of phenomena, affecting perceptible appearances, not hidden structures. It is quite compatible with the transition to a further stage of being.[1]

The enormous problem that evolution sets us is that it seems to save mankind. But, in Teilhard's thought, salvation in the Christian sense is neither eliminated nor replaced. It is the grace of Christ which saves, and not the forces of evolution; yet grace makes use of evolution. *How* it does so, still remains a question, and we cannot attempt to answer it without focusing on it rather more carefully. Before we go into details, let us note that the fundamental position is quite sound; Teilhard is certainly not the only person today to ascribe almost salvific consequences to the world's progress; are we to fear his lending support to those theories (the Marxists', in particular) which transpose the Christian hope—fear that he too may substitute the shadow of this hope for the reality, on the plane of cosmic forces? But Teilhard's concept is utterly different: Christian salvation makes use of natural instruments which *dispose* men to accept God's gifts in a more fitting manner, and thus enable these gifts to bear more fruit. The one essential is not to confuse the disposition to receive with the gift that has been received.

[1] See especially *P*, 169 n.

Let us first define the part played by evolution. A certain ascent takes place, or can take place, with grace or without it, as the result of natural forces, and especially by putting human resources to good use. This fact must be recognized with all its implications. It is not so very long—a couple of hundred years, perhaps, or less—since human consciousness had its first inkling of this, and it is hardly surprising that the knowledge should at times go to its head. *The progressive emancipation of spirit* from the bonds which shackle it; the function of intelligence and freedom; the way in which action can help on this conquest—all these are concepts dear to the modern mind; and they are all true. A passage from Montuclard, for example, expresses them:

> Modern man is convinced that history has a liberating part to play as regards humanity. To him, history is the mediatrix of salvation. And, if he has no religious faith, he carries this conviction to the lengths of believing that it is for history alone—that is to say, for human effort inserted in the historical process —to secure for men, through justice, freedom and solidarity, the deliverance that they seek . . .

> There are, in some men, a faith, a hope, a sense of the future, and at times an overwhelming vision of the historical situation,

from which they can draw self-control, freedom of thought and action, courage and initiative. What did they have to do, in order thus to be "saved"? No more than enter actively into the current of history.[1]

Here, too, is the definition of history:

How else can we describe this great current, apparent nowhere yet diffused everywhere: this current which, all down the ages—influenced in some mysterious way by various determinisms, marked by alternate success and failure, advance and setback—calls forth and makes use of the toil and genius of men, to bring about a flowering of humanism, culture, civilization? There is no secular activity, from the humblest to the noblest, from the simplest to the most heroic, but has the current of history as its source, its impetus, its inspiration, its full range, its final end. No activity can remain outside it; all alike are within it, although some are holding it back and others helping it on its way . . .

Borne on by history, man has it in him to do marvellous things: outside it, he can do nothing.

History is not an abstraction. It is a force, in relation to which man is by no means

[1] Montuclard, "La Médiation de l'Église et la médiation de l'histoire" in *Jeunesse de l'Église*, fasc. 7, "Délivrance de l'homme".

powerless, even though he never has complete control over it. It is history that makes the flowering of talent possible; history which gives the thinker his words, the scientist his instruments, the industrialist his machines. History urges on human society to change and progress; yet it is history again which brings about that interplay of circumstance which leads almost inevitably to crises and wars.

In predicting the advance of mankind towards increased unity and consciousness, Teilhard holds before us a *great hope, common to all*.

There is still to be seen in humanity a reserve of a tremendous potentiality of concentration—in other words, of progress. Think of the immensity of all the forces, ideas, people, that have not yet been discovered, or harnessed, or born, or synthesized.[1]

What relation is there, then, between this hope and Christian hope—between the fecundity of history and the divine vocation of mankind? According to Revelation, God has inaugurated a process of salvation that culminates in the liberation of the soul, in more alert *consciousness*, in interior *freedom*, in the *unity* of men. And, going beyond this, St. Paul and St. John both proclaim that there is a collective body of all the redeemed, a vine which puts forth

[1] *Cité nouvelle*, 10 June 1941.

new shoots as time goes on, and, finally, a *superorganism* still in course of formation, generally known as the Mystical Body of Christ. There is a disturbing similarity of phrase.

(1) In the first place, we must learn to see the distinction that exists between the two processes and their effects. The human group, however closely we may imagine it united by cosmic forces or by our own psychism, is an economic and cultural community, whereas the Mystical Body is animated by sanctifying supernatural life. A communion of all men in the same treasures, whether material, artistic or literary, is as far removed from the Communion of Saints as is human culture from divine love, or civilization from sanctity.

Let us imagine that the movement of history will, to some extent, go astray; that the emancipation of spirit by science and human experience will never quite come off. The building-up of the heavenly Jerusalem will continue, down the centuries, none the less steadily: for it is supernatural love which holds it together, and its completion depends, not on the degree of evolutionary maturity that men have achieved, but on how much sanctity there is among them.

But let us suppose that there will in fact be a glorious liberation of mankind by history, a unity of minds all bent on one common task. Even if we do grant this, that better future for which we are making is still fairly remote; all the generations preceding it, including our own, will have no part in it, or at most see only its first faint outlines. But we know that we are not fated to give only a faint outline of the evangelical virtues. It may be that, in days to come, the work of sanctification will have new resources to draw on (I shall speak of this later); we can, none the less, achieve boundless sanctity even now, and whatever prevents our doing so has nothing to do with the fact that historical evolution is at present incomplete.[1] Evolution has its repercussions on sanctity; let us first see wherein the two orders differ.

A case which throws much light on the question is that of some human being who fulfils all the demands of history—who co-operates, in other words, with the temporal advance of mankind— but who yet falls short of the requirements of God. To be "right with history", so to speak, is not necessarily to be "right with God". Doubtless these two types of perfection are meant to go togther; if we are fully aware that mankind is advancing, we shall feel the need for a tremendous purification of our actions and our whole outlook. Our supernatural acceptance of

[1] Certain difficulties, such as the results of social injustice and excessive poverty, which keep men from putting the Gospels into practice, may be removed in days to come: but there will be others. Bernadette of Lourdes was about as poor as it is possible to be, but her sanctity was none the less great.

God should be even greater than our response to the claims of art or science or action, and all these responses together should combine into a single movement. But it is open to man, even when he is making a genuine effort to attain temporal perfection, to turn in on himself, or take a short view of things, and fail to give God the gift which would save him. His assent to the fullest possibilities of creation can be uttered in the same breath as a "No" of rejection to God the Saviour.

This is a complex situation which cannot be fitted into any scheme of things. The attainment of perfection along the lines of history, and advance in sanctity, are two quite different matters.

(2) Nevertheless growth, whether cosmic or human, in collective organization and the emancipation of spirit is not wholly unconnected with the gradual building-up of the Mystical Body. It is a natural vocation of humanity. We may believe that it is willed by God as something that can serve the total Christ. Its function (if the plan of Providence is adhered to) is probably to predispose man to be incorporated in the supernatural community—to enter the full society of the *agape*.

Assuming a corresponding amount of good will and self-giving to God, it may be argued that the fact of living during a fairly advanced stage of evolution may lead to more alert consciousness and more personal freedom; more-over, the more closely knit the temporal texture of humanity, the more ready man will be to understand the Church. Such conditions favour the growth of a charity that is better fitted to construct the Mystical Body—a charity at once more "communal" and more productive of clear-sighted personal self-commitment. Just as God wants his creatures to be gifted with free will (and, having it in varying degrees, they are capable of varying degrees of praise), so too, it seems, he wants a freedom which grows in intensity and plenitude as the centuries go by. As long as the excesses of mechanization and selfishness do not wreck evolution, the human being of the future will be more closely bound up with his fellows; he will have a sense of great collective unities. The advance of history may make it possible for saints of a new type—saints more whole, more fully complete—to arise. The dangers, however, increase proportionately; there will also be the possibility of more serious sins. But these are the risks of freedom, in which God undoubtedly sees a higher good. Would anyone want to lessen the risks by halting the progress? If we oppose a progress which is willed by nature, it will turn against us.

The subject under discussion calls for fine dis-tinctions. It is posible that there will never be a higher form of sanctity than that of St. Paul, or any other saint one cares to name. The free gift of grace can dispense with human preparations, and, even though it may at times follow their fluctuations, it often shows a regal disregard of them. The most we can say with any degree of probability is this: In so far as the temporal advance of humanity leads to an increase of consciousness, freedom and solidarity, it tends of its very nature to bring about conditions favourable to man's sanctification (although they entail proportionately greater temptations). We must think of it as an element which holds good for all men alike, and which must be judged on an average. And, as we shall see, we cannot rule out the possibility that man's perversity will use the whole potential for the wrong ends.

The movement of history may then, it would seem, help on the salvation of mankind; and this, no doubt, is what it is for. We may see in it an ideal, a hope that is part of the plan of Providence, a proposal put to us by God. Spiritual consequences of great moment are involved in it; the efforts demanded by the purely *temporal* advance of humanity are willed by God the Redeemer, and although some Christians here and there may, on account of their individual vocations, remain more or less aloof, the Christic Body as a whole can claim no such exemption. In so far as we are in our rightful niche in the plan of Providence, carrying out, on all its levels, the work entrusted to us, we shall be at the focal point of the highest possible spiritual fecundity. The progress of mankind will not be brought about automatically, by the mere passage of time: men must fight for it. "If progress is to endure it will not do so of itself. Evolution, by the very nature of its workings, assumes more and more freedom."[1] For the sake of the temporal growth of humanity, we must learn to be enterprising, adventurous, unsparing of ourselves. There ought, among Christians, to be more of the spirit that inspired the great explorers, or those who first tested radium, or founded schools of philosophy. We need many Christians who feel drawn to embrace the common destiny of their generation—of mankind as a whole. And all human achievements, all earthly values—those of believers and unbelievers alike—must be laid at God's feet in a spirit of deep charity by those who know how to pray.

(3) When we remember what men are, and when we think of the appalling part that sin plays in the world, we may well dread some distortion, wrought by sin, of the evolutionary process—a distortion, a reversal, that would threaten the temporal achievement for which mankind yearns. The natural longing for collective advance may, by our own fault, come to nothing; history may move onwards towards de-

[1] From an article quoted in *Cité nouvelle*, 10 June 1941.

personalization, oppression, carnage. But there is also some reason to fear what would be yet more serious: that even *the temporal successes themselves* that we shall probably have achieved may, by common consent, be turned against the supernatural life. The temporal success of the historical process will only serve to promote sanctity if man responds to grace. If he does not, it will lead to an even more disastrous fall.

Let us suppose for a moment that, as far as civilization and temporal peace go, we come very near to achieving total success. Mankind is, on the whole, organized. Wealth is distributed fairly enough. Order prevails, more or less. Intellectual activities are well to the fore; a sufficiently sensitive psychical life is within the reach of many. In such conditions, will the human community choose the love of Christ? Will it encourage any who may choose this love?

It may, perhaps, choose to be sufficient unto itself. It may achieve its unity according to a pagan pattern. Dazzled by the brilliant results before them (although no doubt there will be some fairly serious gaps in their achievements), men may be tempted to make an idol of civilization. It is not hard to picture a planetary life that would be both alluring and non-Christian —not, perhaps, a culture that would meet the highest needs of the spirit; rather, a civilization that would occasionally lead to intellectual and

affective aberrations, such as disquieting manifestations in art and literature; but if there are
already blemishes in the temporal field, they
pass, for the most part, quite unnoticed. It is
perfectly possible for the human community to
live, with quite good results as far as economic
and cultural life are concerned, in a state of open
and avowed hostility to Christianity; or it can
be, quite simply, indifferent—natural rather
than supernatural. Now, collective influences
will probably be of such persuasive force that it
will be very difficult to think and live in a state
of opposition. If this happens—and the prospect
is terrifying—the wonderful cosmic advance towards human perfection will be used for the
undoing of the majority of mankind. It will be
the triumph of the beasts foretold in the Apocalypse.[1] At the topmost peak ever to be scaled
by humanity on this earth, none will be saved
except a few individuals who, for all the pressure of collective influence, still keep faith with
Christ.[2]

[1] These beasts stand respectively for political power
that is pagan and that persecutes, and for intellectual
power—all the ideological influences that ensnare mankind. The drama seems to turn on the fundamental
divergence between collective life and the spirit of
Christ.

[2] This might well be the explanation of the great
apostasy at the end of time, foretold by the Gospels
(Luke 18.8: Matt. 24.11,12: Mark 13.22), by St. Paul (2
Thess. 2.3) and by the Apocalypse (20.7).

According to an idea that turns up constantly in the Bible, it is of the nature of sin to breed. St. Thomas held that if the Incarnation had been delayed until the end of time, all knowledge of God, and all upright conduct, would have vanished off the face of the earth.[1] The process is at work in so far as man interiorly rejects the gift of Christ. There may, then, be two progressions going on simultaneously in the world today: the one, a progression in perversity, the other, in sanctification—a sort of satanic reign becoming increasingly consolidated (although an inner disintegration of man serves to disrupt it) at the same time as the Mystical Body is growing to completion. The contrast between good and evil will become more and more marked—as will the need for Christians to make an unflinching choice.

When we look round us at mankind, pulled this way and that between two trends, we feel it is impossible to say that it will ever take its stand permanently on either good or evil. Perhaps what we shall witness is an endless series of fresh starts, situations which succeed one another in a perpetual skein of ravelling and unravelling, but without any final convergence.

But, if a planetary civilization is set up contrary to the spirit of the Gospels, it will be very difficult to convert it afterwards. It may be that we are standing at the crossroads of humanity,

[1] *Summa*, 3a par. 2.1, 2.6.

where the implicit spiritual choices that we make will be of unforeseeable importance. A vast effort is needed to bring humanity into some sort of harmony with the spirit of Christ.

To sum up: The spiritual perfection of mankind is not the automatic result of evolution. Not only does this perfection come about through an ultra-cosmic force; not only does it depend on a divine gift of another order from that of creation; but this supernatural gift, although it may become incarnate in the things of nature, does not do so in such a way that evolutionary progress *necessarily* leads to an increase in sanctity. True, human nature and sanctity tend to develop alongside; the possibility of (supernatural) salvation is held out to us through evolution—and this positive view is of inestimable importance; but we can refuse the offer of sanctity, or do nothing about it, even while, on the temporal plane, a truly magnificent evolution is going forward.[1] Indeed, we

[1] Here an objection may occur: does this mean that the whole theology of grace has to be reconsidered? After all, we have already revised a concept of the Bible which to Bossuet was sacrosanct. I honestly believe that we must, *on any hypothesis*, make a distinction between natural movement (including the temporal life of the spirit) and supernatural (belonging to the order of sanctification). The unity of the divine plan need not be called in question, for sanctification extends creation, although it introduces new methods. Just as spirit extends life by introducing a new element, with its own

know from experience that advance in evolution
does not invariably coincide with advance in
sanctity.

Did Père Teilhard de Chardin himself see
all that I have just been saying? A certain passage in his writings shows that he was aware of
the danger of a setback, if only partial, in
planetization. The structure of reality destines
mankind to find its perfection in peace, by
cleaving wholly to the glory of Omega; if mankind remains true to this promise, this plan, it
will bring about the convergence of the universe,
in sanctity; but is this really what is going to
happen?

Such an outcome would of course conform
most harmoniously with our theory.

But there is another possibility. Obeying a
law from which nothing in the past has ever
been exempt, evil may go on growing alongside good, and it too may attain its paroxysm
at the end in some specifically new form.

There are no summits without abysses.

Enormous powers will be liberated in mankind by the inner play of its cohesion: though
it may be that this energy will still be em-
ployed discordantly tomorrow, as today and
in the past. Are we to foresee a mechanizing
synergy under brute force, or a synergy of

---

needs, so too does sanctity complete man: but it has its
own laws, of which evolution does not necessarily give
us any idea.

sympathy? Are we to foresee man seeking to fulfil himself collectively upon himself, or personally on a greater than himself? Refusal or acceptance of Omega? A conflict may supervene. In that case the noösphere, in the course of and by virtue of the processes which draw it together, will, when it has reached its point of unification, split into two zones each attracted to an opposite pole of adoration. Thought has never completely united upon itself here below. Universal love would only vivify and detach finally a fraction of the noösphere so as to consummate it—the part which decided to "cross the threshold", to get outside into the other. Ramification once again, for the last time.[1]

Teilhard is here speaking as a naturalist, imagining the various forms of extrapolation possible within the evolutionary process. He may not use the language of the theologian, or appeal to his Christian faith. What he says is eloquent enough; and there is no more that he can say.

On the other hand, a certain footnote which really is on the theological level calls for some clarification: "For a Christian believer it is interesting to note that the final success of hominization (and thus cosmic involution) is positively guaranteed by the 'redeeming virtue' of

[1] *P*, 288–9.

the God incarnate in his creation. But this takes us beyond the plane of phenomenology."[1] What is guaranteed by Christian doctrine is the success of the *supernatural* Pleroma; this does not necessarily imply the unification of mankind in a natural superorganism, or a change of state brought to a successful conclusion, or the attainment of a second "point of reflection". It is not, to Christians, a "matter of life or death that earth should flourish to the uttermost of its natural powers."[2] We may not say, "God willed that he should have need of it."[3] Grace can do without the triumphs of nature, although, when they do occur, it makes use of them; we must do what we can to further them, but the fulfilment of Christ's promises is in no way threatened, even if the triumphs are wanting. Were mankind to come to an end tomorrow, the supernatural Pleroma, or Mystical Body, would still be complete; the saints of all the ages would be united to Christ and to one another; the properties of supernatural life would suffice to make them one body, quite independently of any new event in the natural order. The idea of a natural convergence is a hypothesis; there is nothing in Christian teaching to substantiate it. If the hypothesis is true: if mankind is really destined to be built up into a hyper-person, there is nothing to guarantee the success of this process either.

[1] *P*, 308 *n*. [2] *M*, 42.
[3] *M*, 43.

We may, however, believe that the Pleroma will use for its own ends that degree of success within the natural order of unity and consciousness that the true friends of God have managed to achieve.

It is quite true to say that "each one of our works, by its more or less remote or direct effect on the spiritual world, helps to make perfect Christ in His mystical totality".[1] And again, "God is inexhaustibly attainable in the *totality* of our action."[2] The sanctity of a creature lies in fulfilling the "exact function, be it lowly or eminent, to which [it] is destined both by natural endowment and by supernatural gift."[3] But certain other expressions in Teilhard's writings are exaggerated or ambiguous, as when he says: "By pressing the stroke, the line, or the stitch on which I am engaged, to its ultimate natural finish, I shall lay hold of that last end towards which my innermost will tends."[4] This attainment of the supernatural end is of course quite compatible with perfect human activity; indeed, in certain spiritual conditions, such activity helps to promote it; but it is never the cause of it. The source from which it flows is a gift of God, to be found more often in prayer, sacramental life, the study of the Bible. And unless one drinks often from these springs, one's work tends to grow meaningless and gradually lose all its supernatural power.

[1] *M*, 34.   [2] *M*, 36.
[3] *M*, 39.   [4] *M*, 37.

There is, too, a certain ambiguity in what Teilhard has to say of the impermanence of temporal achievements; he will not allow that the works of men, the discoveries, the glories of art, "perish for ever."[1] He insists that the *result* of our labours must, in some way, be eternalized, redeemed[2]; he seems to suggest that the world, once man has set it to rights, will be ready, just as it is, for the resurrection.[3] But how very uncertain all this is, and how ill-advised we should be to cherish so perilous a hope! Elsewhere he has something far better to say; it is by our toils on this earth, he tells us, that our personal powers of knowing and loving are formed. "We hardly know in what proportions and under what guise our natural faculties will pass over into the final act of the vision of God."[4] But "with God's help it is here below that we give ourselves the eyes and heart which a final transfiguration will make the organs of a power of adoration . . . particular to each individual man and woman among us."[5] In a letter to P. Valensin, Teilhard expresses the same idea:

I do not attribute any definitive or absolute value to the varied constructions of nature.

[1] *M*, 26.   [2] *M*, 26.
[3] See *M*, 151. But it would no doubt be a misrepresentation of the author's thought to insist too much on such phrases.
[4] *M*, 31.   [5] *M*, 47.
7+

What I like about them is not their particular
form, but their function, which is to build
up mysteriously, first what can be divinised,
and then, through the grace of Christ coming
down upon our endeavour, what is divine . . .[1]

We will agree, then, that Père Teilhard de
Chardin's true thought is best expressed in these
completely traditional formulas. We may indeed
wish that he had carried his theological reflections a little further. The truths that he reveals
can only be understood aright if a correct solution is found for the problems raised by their
comparative novelty. We can dispense with the
final subtleties of definition in which the theological mind so often delights; but it is essential,
in the first place, to get the matter in focus; and
often enough this is not done.

Finally, I am quite sure that Teilhard's
opinions rest on a firm foundation—a foundation which he was the first to see for what it was.
His fundamental argument may be summed up
under two headings:

(1) Mankind is invited, by its natural structure, to achieve more and more unity and consciousness.

(2) Inasmuch as this progress in the natural
order leads to a certain predisposition, it is possible to use it in such a way as to help on the

[1] M, 74. But there are not two successive times. We
should build up, with Christ, something that *is*, in an
increasingly marked manner, divine.

full flowering of supernatural life (and consequently the attainment of the Christic Pleroma).

It may be added that the life of grace serves even the process of nature, by giving men—in the best cases—a union of charity and wisdom of soul for which, even on the natural plane, there is no substitute.

It seems fairly pointless to discuss the shortcomings in Teilhard's argument. The final clarifications that he fails to give us may be supplied by others. He is so great that he may be forgiven for not having seen everything. He opens horizons that we never dreamed of. It is for us to ponder the truth that he was the first to discover, and so come gradually to see all its theological implications.

The idea of a cosmic Christ is linked up with the concepts that have already been discussed. I shall not insist on it overmuch, for it is a subject fraught with dangers and difficulties.

St. Paul and the Greek Fathers saw Christ as fulfilling a cosmic function. The exact meaning of these words has perhaps never been elucidated. Is it possible that Teilhard gives us the clue?

To him, the universe is convergent, and Christ is at its centre.[1] When mankind (or part of the mankind that is to be) achieves its unification and becomes welded into a new, natural

[1] *P*, 297.

personality, there Christ will be, right at the centre of convergence. By supernaturalizing this human group, he will complete the ascent of evolution; he will, indeed, bring it to a state of perfection of which, by nature, it had no inkling.[1] Then there will be only God, who is "all in all". And, since he is there at the end of evolution, Christ is drawing, and has been drawing, all things to him, ever since the process first began; he "put himself in the position (maintained ever since) to subdue under himself, to purify, to direct and superanimate the general ascent of consciousness into which he had inserted himself".[2] Cosmogenesis is "Christified" down to its very roots.[3]

These formulas call for at least two sets of comments:

1. Christ's action is supernatural—distinct, therefore, from the ascent of evolution. This ascent will culminate in a "world ripe for conversion".[4] The work of the salvific Incarnation *is based on* "a natural human unity, the preparation and foundation of the higher unity *in Christo Jesu*".[5] On these points, Teilhard's writings are clear enough; evolution, as it is in the concrete, and despite the fact that it is animated by Christ, cannot of itself "Christify" mankind. If, at some future date, evolution works out to

[1] *P*, 297.　　　　　　[2] *P*, 294.
[3] *A*, 374.　　　　　　[4] *V*, 196.
[5] *V*, 193.

a successful conclusion, the problem of conversion (to Christ) will still be there, and still as urgent as ever. There will never be such a thing as an irresistible grace that mankind accepts joyously, without first having to clear the hurdle of making a choice; even when evolution is at its peak, mankind will still have the responsibility of choosing; and it may well be that temptation will be proportionately greater.[1]

When we speak of the cosmic Christ, this does not imply that the Incarnation extends throughout the universe. The Incarnation, correctly speaking, relates to the man Jesus, and to him alone. He takes to himself a body which we call mystical—a body made up of the union of all human beings who live by the supernatural life. This body, of which we already have the embryonic beginnings, will grow through the ages; it is not a new Incarnation—unless, indeed, we use the word in an extended sense, in which case it should be spelt with a small letter; the incarnation, in human beings, of divine life (which in them becomes supernatural life) is not regarded as "theandric". But such verbal juggling, common enough today, is to be avoided, for it leads to confusion. Still less is the universe a body in which the Word becomes incarnate. We must be careful not to imagine that there is

[1] Certain over-optimistic phrases suggest that, once the Omega-Point is seen, mankind will cling to it in one mystical ardour. This, doubtless, is the ideal. . . .

such a thing as a "pan-Christism", in which everything contains a fragment of Christ. Christ is *linked* with the cosmos, but the universe is not, and never will be, a vaster Incarnation of him. It is better, then, not to speak of "a silently accruing presence of Christ in things".[1] Earth is not (even if we add "beyond itself") "the body of him who is and him who is coming."[2] There is no such thing as a cosmic Host; the phrase has only a metaphorical meaning, and is too misleading to be retained. The universe is an extension of the body of Christ; this concept, which is very profound, is well worth elaboration; but we must be careful to distinguish the body of Christ from its adjuncts. And the insistence on the physical or biological reality of the Mystical Body is also misleading; the vital (and real) bonds which unite it are all supernatural. The cosmos, and animal life, are clearly not part of the Mystical Body or the total Christ. Yet they are not outside the movement which leads to it. There is a *dynamic unity* in the divine plan; beings of very different natures are taking part together in one all-embracing process whose

[1] *M*, 147.

[2] *M*, 153. There is a similar ambiguity in the following passage: "We shall never know what the Incarnation still expects of the world's potentialities." (*M*, 152.) The sanctifying work of the salvific Incarnation uses the forces of the world as instruments; and in this sense it may be said to await their predisposing of our souls. But that is all.

culmination, through Christ, is steeped in supernatural life. The total Christ is thus the *goal*
of all creation. And hence there will come about
a unity which does not imply any loss of identity.
We already knew that this unity of all things was
that of a divine plan to be fulfilled in the
heavenly Jerusalem; Teilhard de Chardin has
shown us that it is also that of a progressive
movement, for the whole process of evolution is
tending to the formation of a sanctified mankind.
The first groupings of matter, then the first
living organisms, were, in God's plan, far-off
preparations for the coming of the Pleroma; and
the collective continuation of evolution ever
since man's first appearance on earth has some
part to play in bringing about the supernatural
perfection of the human group. When we say
that Christ draws all things to himself, we must
not, then, think of any physical action (i.e., any
natural action, of a cosmic nature) which would
give the universe final cohesion.[1] Beyond the
sphere of supernatural actions, which affect
mankind alone, there is, as far as the universe
is concerned, only movement towards an end:
the creative mind so frames the universe as to
enable it to *serve* the attainment of sanctity.
Christ draws men to him by a spiritual attraction. Since man sums up the cosmos, and com-

[1] It should be noted that the words quoted by St.
John (12.32)—"I will draw all things to myself"—refer,
in all probability, only to man.

pletes the process of evolution, it may be said that in him the universe is drawn to Christ; what is here meant is the very special "pull" of the Last End, affecting man's physical participation in the cosmos and evolution. Thus the universe may well disappear, once its work is done; or else another and quite different universe may be the setting of those who have risen again. Let us not unduly praise the present economy of things. Christian teaching calls, I think, for certain distinctions.

10

THE QUESTIONS OF CHRISTIANS: CONTACT WITH THE WORLD

MERELY to evolve is not man's final end. Evolution does not automatically usher us into the order of divine life; nor does it confer on us the love with which God loves—the love that we must have if we are to be saved. The mediation of history has no sacramental character. To the man who lives by grace, evolution may be an ally, in that it predisposes the human being and thus contributes something to the work of his spiritual perfection; but it can never actually be the cause of this perfection.[1] The spiritual efficacy is at its highest with the greatest grace. Each one of us, living as he does at a given moment in history, can only evolve within certain limits, and perhaps the ideal is not to go to the utmost extreme in this direction, for there are certain dangers in an over-rapid evolution; it may throw

[1] The unbeliever who does all that lies in him, but who has none of the ordinary means of obtaining supernatural life, can be saved by trying whole-heartedly to remain true to history. It is not evolution that saves him, but a grace (supernatural life) coming from God.

us off our balance. The branch of a fruit-tree grows as time goes on; we do not ask of it to grow as fast as possible: all we want is that, at whatever stage it is, it should bear fruit. It is by *what we are* at the present moment (and what gifts we have from God) that we can build something positive; what we are includes a *trend* towards the future, as also a proximity to the cosmos and an openness to the society in which we live. This is what makes the question so complex, and why the solution to it has to be so subtly worked out. It is not our drive towards the future that determines our worth; yet this is likely to lack something unless we are in fact moving in the direction of history. A ship should not depend on its speed to keep it on the water, as does a stone in a game of ducks-and-drakes; but it should move, none the less, and its very movement may steady it. Evolution has no power to save; but our salvation will be more assured if we accept, each to the measure of his capacity, history, the universe, the social structure.

Teilhard's disciples err if they forget the overwhelming importance of keeping in touch with God by those means best suited to the purpose— prayer, the sacraments, meditation on the Bible, the liturgy, invocation of the saints, etc. They are right in so far as they do not keep these means sealed off from that profound immersion in the cosmos and human life that should be theirs. All this, of course, is no new teaching. Christ practised both aspects of life.

The man with a sense of evolution grows immensely in stature.

His life, in a true sense, ceases to belong to him alone. He comes forth, body and soul, from a vast creative labour in which, from the beginning of time, the whole totality of things has been collaborating; if he shirks the task assigned to him, something of that effort will be lost for ever—lacking for all time to come. O holy emotion of the atom, when it sees in its depths the face of the universe![1]

Man's progress is not favoured by isolation.[2] His duty is coextensive with the world, and particularly with the world of men. We must rediscover "the sense of, the ruling passion for, the All".[3]

In us and around us, almost visible to the naked eye, a psychological phenomenon of vast import is taking place, a phenomenon that came into existence barely a hundred years ago, and that may be called *the awakening of the human sense*. Men are beginning to feel that they are all without exception bound to an immense task, the progress of which holds them under an almost religious spell. To know more, to increase one's

[1] *V*, 191.　　　　　　　[2] Cf. *P*, 263.
[3] *V*, 195.

capacity! These words, although to many they still have a utilitarian ring, are, to most of us, haloed with a sacred significance. Men, today, think nothing of giving their lives "for the advance of mankind".[1]

Some Christians, out of laziness, or out of concern for their own virtue, barely touch this great human task with so much as a finger-tip.[2] Yet to enter fully into our function as men— and this includes its temporal aspects—brings a greater meaning, an "added soul"[3] into all things, and into our own lives; and, if our attention has been drawn to that need we have for sanctity, the desire for being, strengthened by study of temporal things, will become increasingly a desire for the divine.[4] By action which follows the outlines of reality, as well as by the passivities which accompany such action, we come to know being, to learn more and more about its laws and the conditions governing its fulfilment. All this, Teilhard has pointed out magnificently. Our nature, fashioned as it is to receive divine life, may in fact become more responsive; and it is the task of all culture, all civilization, all training of the heart and mind, even in non-religious matters, to make it so. Certain forms of lay progress can, if we know how to use them, help us to grow more mature,

[1] V, 241. [2] M. 22.
[3] M, 127.
[4] M, and especially 120–3.

less narrow, trivial and childish; and, by comparison, to put the problem of salvation in a better perspective.

It is not enough to speak of Christian humanism, or even of the sanctifying merit of lay work. To Teilhard, it is the collective and objective aspect of temporal progress that is so important. There can no longer be any question of polishing up one's own soul into something beautiful and useless; but we still have to build up our souls, inserting them into the movement of history and the movement of mankind towards the total Christ. There is a marvellous amplitude about the work. Our spirituality is firmly grounded on the positive, on the good to be done; we shed our scruples and faint-heartedness, abandon those castles in the air in which an over-interiorized preoccupation with spirituality sometimes takes refuge. In this new state of affairs, there is both gain and risk; the good is no longer something abstract and impalpable; it is made manifest, it becomes almost tangible, so deeply is our sensibility impressed by the twin themes of evolution and social construction. And this would constitute a danger if we were indifferent to those values which transcend history. Indeed, it may so happen—not that these higher values run counter to evolution in its main line of ascent, but that to some extent they condemn history, as men cause it to be. Our spirituality will be all the better for our feeling the urgency of progress. But we must rid ourselves of all restlessness; we must not, out of idle curiosity, let ourselves become obsessed by new forms soon to be cast aside. If only to discern the main trend of evolution and the line along which man is now called to advance, we should learn to sit light to passing realities. This calls for certain virtues—maturity of mind, hope, a sense of the more durable; true, this is not the whole of Christian detachment, but it blazes the trail for it, and the rest may follow.[1]

When our mental gaze finds its true object— the perfection of the human-Christic body now in process of formation—our whole enquiry takes on a more direct orientation; we have always been going astray, and now at last we are on the right track. It will never again be possible for the individual to see himself as the centre, or to look no further than his own tiny world. But this newly found sense of liberation grows stronger still, the more we realize our contact— our immediate contact—with the salvation of God. We need not wait for planetization before

[1] There are some very fine passages on detachment through action in M, 44-7. "The interest lies truly *in* things but in absolute dependence on God's presence in them." (p. 46.) What is meant is a presence of sanctification.

There are also some excellent pages on detachment through passivity. (M, 51-74, 77-82.) (But I do not think that the problem of evil has been sufficiently tackled.)

Christian salvation can bear fruit in us. Teilhard knows this, and at one point says forcefully, "Lastly, is it not also a fact, as I can warrant, that if the love of God were extinguished in the souls of the faithful, the enormous edifice of rites, of hierarchy and of doctrines that comprise the Church would instantly revert to the dust from which it rose?"[1] Here too there is, in the order of phenomena, a fact given to experience: and to lose sight of it would be to distort the meaning of Teilhard's observations.

I believe, then, that the solution adopted is entirely legitimate. This solution may be thus summarized: To seek both God and the advance of evolution; and to do all that God asks of us, which includes fulfilling the demands that evolution makes on us. I also grant this principle: Sanctification completes and prolongs the evolutionary ascent. We may note that, according to St. Thomas, sanctification completes and prolongs creation; and, as creation develops through evolution, the whole thing hangs together perfectly. But if we are to apply this principle aright, we must bear in mind two important points:

(1) Sanctification has its own means and its own imperatives, which transcend evolution and cannot be found in it.

[1] *P*, 295–6.

(2) Sanctification prolongs the main trend of evolution (which is the achievement of being) in its objective aspect, but not, perhaps, in man's idea of it. That which, to our contemporaries, seems to conform with the trend of history does not necessarily conform with sanctity. As human psychism interprets it, the evolutionary ascent is weighed down with contingencies and betrayals; man may be quite out in his calculations, even if he is looking to the future not only about the political forms which seem to him most favourable, but about the spirit and methods of science; still more, he may be deceived as to the highest form of spirituality, which pride may hide from him, or his delusive whims, or his lack of perception.

A fundamental Christian reflection should be able to supplement the views of Teilhard's, correct as they are; many are the conflicts that arise between nature and the Kingdom of God. If we looked no further than the great structures of the world and the human being, we might suppose that the transition from nature to grace would take place quite smoothly; creation disposes everything in such a way that the crowning gift of supernatural life ought to arouse no opposition. But in fact, *nature resists grace*; it dreads the transformation asked of it—the transformation which it sees simply as a troublesome intrusion, clashing with all its cherished habits. *Grace leaves nature no peace*; hustles it, pushes it about. The Old Man will never give way to the New without a certain degree of heroism; we have to face the fact that all our instinctive ideas will be radically altered, our whole system of life disrupted, our self refashioned, all human wisdom held suspect. Yet all this is not a condemnation of nature; it does but provide the concrete conditions in which nature is made perfect.

We must not, then, without submitting them to careful scrutiny, accept those impulses which today seem to us natural and well able to build up the future, and turn them into a form of spirituality. The temptation to do so is by no means imaginary; we say to ourselves that we'll go in for sport, science, technics; throw in a bit of poetry or music or comparative literature; add quite a strong dash of social welfare; flavour with a vague mystical concept of a Christified universe; and—there we are; we've found the recipe for salvation. But none of this is of the slightest use unless it has behind it a sanctifying force from on high; and this is held out to us, but we must use the means of making it our own. Two spheres are particularly significant: our contact with the universe, our relations with our fellows.

All Teilhard's works leave one general impression on our minds: how enormously important matter is to spirit.

Matter, you in whom I find both seduction and strength, you in whom I find blandishment and virility, you who can enrich and destroy, I surrender myself to your mighty layers, with faith in the heavenly influences which have sweetened and purified your waters. The virtue of Christ has passed into you.[1]

One sees what the author had in mind when he wrote those words; but, as they stand, they seem to me deplorable. Matter is dangerous, and Redemption has not drained it of its poison. We must not—to change the metaphor—listen to the echoes of this siren voice within us, without taking care to distinguish the true accents from the false. Yet, when all is said, nature has in fact positive values, of which we should be foolish to deprive ourselves. Any human life which tries to develop in isolation from the material world, or having as little to do with it as possible, is simply courting illusion. We are in our rightful place, and making full use of the resources of evolution, if we sum it up, in all its fulness, in ourselves; if we feel the unity of the cosmos. For the cosmos may be a source of strength and light *to the spirit.* It is not just a matter of the poetry of the universe, real enough though this is, and seen most clearly by those who gaze at it throughout a lifetime. We need

[1] *M*, 129.

a spirituality that is in touch with nature.[1] It is not enough to see spirit in the ascent of evolution. We have to learn to draw spiritual nourishment from minerals, fossils, bits of wood, living animals. Between such raw material and religious life, the study of science is an obvious intermediary; but so too are work on the land, industry, and art in all its forms. None of this will lead automatically to spiritual progress, but it can all be a contributing factor, for those who hearken to the voice of God.

Human research is a communal thing, although it implies a multiplicity of individual initiatives and innumerable separate trends of thought. There are outstanding values, which call for recognition, in communal work as such. *"A tremendous spiritual power is slumbering in the depths of our multitude, which will manifest itself only when we have learnt to break down the barriers of our egoisms and, by a fundamental recasting of our outlook, raise ourselves up to the habitual and practical vision of universal realities."* [2] The world is a workshop in which Christians should do their honest share. To urge this is not to go back on the condemnation of the world uttered in the Gospels, for what is there condemned is a frivolous or sinful form of life, whose aim it is to seek pleasure

[1] And this is just what the psalms give us.
[2] *M*, 139–40.

from the universe rather than to fulfil any function in it; hence "the world", in this context, stands for a system of objects and behaviour leading to sin. But when mankind unites to build up civilization, it is doing something which can be turned to good account by the Christic body. "Cut yourself off from the world," Père Gratry used to say, "but never from mankind."[1] Collaboration in any honest work helps us to "recognize in one another members of the same deeply desired being".[2] The unbeliever too is called, by such means as are open to him, to become part of the mystical body of Christ. If, as a result of working together Christians come to regard unbelievers, too, as their brothers, the moment is ripe for true conversion.

Christians and unbelievers are not, of course, pursuing the same ends. Unbelievers are aiming at temporal prosperity; Christians, at the perfection of the Gospels. But, as has often been said (particularly by Maritain), what, to a pagan, is the *final aim*, to a Christian is an *intermediate one*—always assuming that what is in question is a true human good; and thus it is possible to carry out in common a programme which, as far as the Christian is concerned, can never fulfil *all* his desires, but which may well be a means of attaining the higher good that is the object of his quest. Let us learn, then, to develop a

[1] *Les Sources.*
[2] *V,* 192.

strong sense of all that we have in common, all
that unites us to other men, without in the least
trying to whittle away the differences between
them and ourselves. Why should the clear-
sightedness that sees these differences prevent us
from seeing also the enthusiasm, the ardour,
shared by all alike, and which should rule out
all possibility of segregation? I am grateful to
Teilhard for having recognized the diversity,
becoming ever more marked, of the human
group; and for having pointed out the active
sympathy, stronger than was ever known, that
underlies it. The simultaneity of the two elements (differentiation: unity) is a condition of
progress.

Once this is clearly seen, the drama becomes
all the more tense. Mankind is spiritually torn:
efforts, such as the achievements of science,
which on the temporal level are wholly admirable, may, if those directing them have twisted
minds, be turned against supernatural good. We
must, then, recognize how misleading is the well-
known saying, "All things that ascend, converge." No; not all things are pursuing the same
end. It is possible for an upward trend to turn
aside from the supernatural goal. But all right
things converge, if what we have in mind is that
fundamental rightness which, in the last analysis,
is the rightness of our relationship with God,
even if God is quite unknown to us; the
righteous act of the unbeliever comes together

supernaturally with that of the Christian. It may so happen that one or other misses his footing and fails to keep up with the march of history; in that case the convergence is harder to see. Conversely, there may be, deep down in successful temporal collaboration, essential as it is, occasional blemishes, of which God alone is judge. But this comment should not serve as a pretext for making bad worse, which is what would happen if unbelievers became unable to meet Christians in any true sense.

We must state things as they are. Teilhard's approach, which seems to me quite legitimate, makes it impossible for Christians to shirk a serious debate—a debate engendered by the yearning for unity—with unbelievers. There will soon be upon us a searching confrontation of religion with the movement of lay knowledge. This will doubtless end in a purification of religion: but what difficulties we shall encounter first!

This confrontation is to be desired, and I see no reason why we should dread it. It has never yet taken place on any deep level. Unhappily, most Christians—even, most theologians—are unable to engage unbelievers in debate in any way that serves a useful purpose; and unbelievers come to such debates quite as unprepared as Christians. It would be very risky to set even the boldest Christian on to tackling problems to which he was unequal. But the

Christian community should learn to see its own lack of preparedness, and lose no time in finding a remedy.

Taking Teilhard's thought as our starting-point, we have two lines open to us. Either we retain his most important conclusions, while supplementing them by views deeply coloured by religion—in which case we shall achieve an utterly honest Christianity that is more vital than ever; or, shifting the main preoccupation of religion onto another object, we shall pursue evolutionary progress instead of sanctity, and in so doing hit on a substitute for Christianity with little of religion about it, and thus lose our finest Christian intuitions.

The temptation would be to reduce religion to cosmic achievement, and never pass beyond it to that which transcends the cosmos and man. There is only one question that haunts the Christian: our whole life, whether we advert to the thought or not, is a choice—for God, or against him; our whole life sets us in a relation to God—a relation that we may render false; and it is precisely the truth or falsity of this relation that constitutes our deepest being. A deviation—sin—on this level is something entirely different from mere lack of evolution. And, conversely, it is not from cosmic progress that the light of sanctity streams. Herein lies a dramatic vision of the world, and it is one that

Teilhard stresses very little; the rise or fall of men takes place invisibly, and the ascent of evolution does not come into the matter. Herein also lies the importance of the religious order, as such. A martyr is hopelessly frustrated as far as the cosmos and all its gifts are concerned, yet he is united with God; and every Christian is, to some degree, in this violent and paradoxical, but very instructive, position. He has to go to God direct, with or without any thought of the universe; then, all the rest is added unto him, but by a sort of overflow.

To ignore cosmogenesis in the name of the supernatural would be quite the wrong attitude. But let us not, in our reaction against an a-cosmic approach, fall into the opposite error of transposing the mysteries of salvation on to a cosmic plane. To do this would be to distort Père Teilhard de Chardin's intention; it is not he who lies open to the reproach incurred by such thinking, but certain over-hasty readers of his works. There is a danger in wanting to make the mysteries of Christianity more tangible, for their reality is not of a kind that can be handled. Physical realities have spiritual bearings; but the central reality of religion is not of the same stuff as even human evolution.

If our only interest is in evolution, we shall never be religious. We must take an intense interest in that which is the specific act of Christ —sanctification. We must love the Gospel virtues in all their stark simplicity, have a sense of the cross of Christ and of certain virtues that go with it—modesty; love of the contemplative life (which means a gaze riveted on God); the longing for God's friendship. If Christians fail to see the difference between the attraction exercised by Christ and the attraction of evolution, the result will be disastrous; but we may set out from the attraction of evolution, come gradually to see its ultimate meaning, realize that it has to be transcended and made over to something greater than itself; and thus, finally, come to Christ.

The *doctrines* of sin and redemption are compatible with Teilhard's views. But if the *responsiveness* to these facts is lost, the doctrinal knowledge will remain inoperative. For instance, it is not enough to bandy about the word "incarnation"; we have to feel the unique nature of incarnation in Christianity—above all, the gratuitous, unlooked-for descent of God's salvation into an earthly setting that is weak and ill-prepared.[1] That we are on the track of new types of sanctity—this is excellent; assuming that we do not lose the specific attributes of religion.

On this condition, there is much to be gained from putting Teilhard's ideas in practice. Laying aside those of his hypotheses that are over-daring,

[1] We know how strongly Karl Barth has stressed this idea. Indeed, Teilhard's treatment of it needs to be supplemented and corrected by that of Barth.

we shall retain a trend of thought and action that will give us much. We must labour at the task of carrying human evolution to its completion, without ever losing sight of its cosmic roots, and keeping steadily in view the end it should be serving—the reign of Christ.

11

THE GREAT SYNTHESIS

THE religious writings of Père Teilhard de Chardin consist, precisely, in a synthesis of the teaching of St. Paul, and the theory of evolution. In some way as yet obscure, the whole cosmos is in expectation of that new order in which the universe will be under Christ's dominion; all things will attain their fulness when Christ, uniting with himself in one body all the redeemed, reigns supreme over the world and delivers it to his Father.[1] This is the teaching that Teilhard is defining when he tells us that evolution in general is continued by the evolution of man. But he defines rather too much, for his views are most open to question where they are most determinate—on the structure of a human super-organism, regarded as an instrument, a state of readiness, at the service of God's kingdom. Let us reserve this delicate question

[1] "And he hath subjected all things under his feet, and hath made him head over all the church, which is ... the fulness of him who is filled all in all." (Eph. 1.22–3.) Cf. Rom. 8.19; 1 Cor. 15.20–8; Phil. 3.21; Col. 1.20; Heb. 2.5–8.

for the time being, and see in what way evolution, prolonged by the progress of mankind, can help us to a better understanding of St. Paul's thesis.

Père Teilhard de Chardin sets before us the plan of Providence, which may be summed up as "the return of the creature to God". Creatures are called to approach God as closely as they can. According to St. Thomas, "to approach" means to share more fully, to grow more like absolute being; and, in the case of man, to receive the life of God within himself. Teilhard insists that there will be a unification of all creation in one increasingly coherent whole, which, at its summit (the mystical body of the elect), will culminate in close communion with God. He traces the unfolding of consciousness from its cosmic beginnings up to the attainment of the Omega-Point. The whole universe is advancing towards human consciousness and the total Christ. And thus the return of creatures becomes more perceptible: evolution sets it before us. To begin with, creation produced none but rudimentary effects; then it became organized and more sharply defined; and all its progress is so ordained as to lead up to the final Pleroma. There, through Christ, and through a reunited mankind. "God will be all in all." The cosmos is in expectation, because the work in which the whole universe is taking part is not yet complete; it will find its perfection when

Christ not only submits all things to himself, but unites them. Unites them by the supernatural bond linking him with the human community, which itself is bound up with the cosmos, not only through men's bodies, but by the place it holds at the end of the long process of construction.

It is all one vast movement towards the highest possible degree of consciousness and unity. And the highest degree of consciousness is communion with God. Let us first see the identity between two aspects which men today tend to dissociate—the integrity of the creature and his union with the Creator. The cosmos, and man himself, find the full attainment of their being at the precise moment when they open completely to God. Cosmogenesis is a simultaneous advance towards personalization and towards a totality which, if it is to receive its fulness of being, lays down as a condition that man should "lose" himself in God; but this losing oneself must take place in the sense given to it by love; then, far from merging into loss of identity, the being at last becomes supremely personal.[1] The meeting of all consciousness in Omega will carry each one to its highest point. Thus the purely natural movement of contraction is prolonged by supernatural forces, through

[1] I refer the reader to *Le Milieu divin*, where these ideas are treated more fully.

which this movement attains a wholly unlooked for completion—unlooked-for, but no doubt implicit in, the advance of evolution, or, at any rate, in profound harmony with it.

Teilhard takes up, but modifies, a concept current in the East—as, indeed, the Thomist notion of the return to God had already done. The Eastern mind commonly sees reality as a sun surrounded by rays, each of which loses something of its brilliance the further it goes from its centre, until finally it is nothing; yet it is precisely there that it is most differentiated. Individuation, then, is a decline, and the one hope of salvation for man lies in a return to that state of indistinction from which he started. Teilhard sees that the creature should return to the centre; he conceives of a vast return, beginning with the formation of atoms, then bringing about increasing concentrations of consciousness, interiorizing men and welding humanity together, and culminating in fusion with God; but, there, the highest point of unity and coherence is also the highest point of personalization.

The product as it is of cosmogenesis, mankind, by becoming "Christified", completes that process of involution which the cosmos began. Whether or not earth is doomed to perish, every human soul will, in the course of its earthly life, have undergone a gradual training in symbiosis with the universe, in which cosmic resources and universal involution have played their part in bringing him to perfection. And in this work —this supernatural, imperishable work—Christified mankind and the cosmos will have collaborated to the utmost. The building up of the Mystical Body will make use not only of natural structures (this we knew already) but of the *advance* of creation. The time of Christ's taking possession of the universe has been in preparation ever since the first workings of evolution; it begins with the cosmogenesis of the biologist and the physicist.

We must, though briefly, deal with a difficulty which lies at the very heart of Teilhard's synthesis. This synthesis is based on a universal principle: the completion of evolution coincides with the Mystical Body made up of Christ and his saints. This principle may be understood in a fairly indeterminate manner, which would be quite enough to achieve the synthesis; we need, in fact, say no more than that the culmination of evolution is a sanctified humanity, without trying to define the type of unity that this would imply. Now, what Teilhard stresses is the superorganism to be made up (according to him) of assembled humanity.

It seems quite clear from his writings that this superorganism, "the brain of brains", will be the *natural* result of *natural* causes. It will be "Christified"—that is, supernaturalized—by the presence of Christ; but what is to be offered for this Christification is a vast, hyperpersonal unity. Of those labouring to form this higher unity, many, no doubt, are animated by supernatural life; and this life is, therefore, one of the factors contributing to planetization. The organism to be built will not be supernaturalized all at once, as soon as it is completed. But underlying the complexity of inspirations and energies engaged in the work, we must learn to detect the natural order; planetization is a human assemblage; the new unity being formed is in itself no more supernatural than a chemical experiment or a psychological discovery made by a Christian. The natural result of the new assemblage will serve the Christic Pleroma as a basis, as matter to be informed, as a channel well adapted for conveying the fulness of grace—rather as, according to the Thomist theory, the organized body is the matter of the soul. The evolution of animals has produced a human body capable of receiving a spiritual soul; in the same way, although on another level, the evolution of man is gradually organizing the collective Person capable of supporting the Pleroma. It will be, in Teilhard's view, a real human person, made up of men, just as our bodies are made up of cells.

This idea seems to me quite unwarranted either by science or by religion. But even if we reject it, the synthesis still holds good: and this is the point that I am anxious to make. Neither the Gospels nor St. Paul said anything about a "brain of brains". What St. Paul had in mind was a supernatural unity, a texture woven throughout by grace. Nor was the heavenly Jerusalem of St. John held together of itself, but by Christ. If this is so—if it is the supernatural life of Christ that causes organic unity where, without it, there would be disintegration—it is probably true that no purely natural assemblage can be formed. The argument from St. Paul tells, on the whole, *against* the idea of a natural superorganism.

There is, it is true, one other interpretation. God sets going an ascending movement of the whole, which, at different levels, needs very different means. Towards the end, when the time comes to reunite mankind in a collective personality, the means required are supernatural. Teilhard speaks of the attraction exerted by Omega—the chief factor of unity in mankind's last period.[1] According to this conception, it is impossible for evolution to come to a successful

[1] See especially *A*, 358–9. Most of the passages in question, however, lead one to think of a natural super-organism. "God willed that he should have need of it" (a successful earthly outcome, a super-humanity, *M*, 43). A "world undergoing psychical concentration" will end by achieving unity in harmonized complexity. (*P*. 262.) The "brain of brains" (*Études*, May 1916, p. 162), etc. Perhaps these passages, treating of the subject as they

conclusion without grace; but God has resolved
to complete his work, using the supernatural
means required for the purpose. There is, therefore, a wonderful unity of phenomena, which
shows the coherence of God's plan; and, simultaneously, ontological breaks in the causes at
work. A kind of natural desire for completion
runs through the whole universe; now, perfect
completion is nothing other than the Mystical
Body. The fact that grace is a free gift is not
called in question, if we allow that humanity, in
its state of evolution, is striving towards final
unification—which does not mean that the
whole thing comes to nothing unless the unity
to be achieved is that of a Person, supernaturally
constituted.

According to this concept, there is no natural
superorganism; evolution culminates in the

_____

do from the purely phenomenal standpoint, should not
be over-insisted on.

In either case, what has been said (ch. 9, pp. 170–80)
still remains true. (1) We must distinguish natural processes, and their specific results, from supernatural.
(2) They are made to be united. (3) Their union will
never be perfect, and the possibility of serious diver-
gences cannot be ruled out.

All natural progress in unity and consciousness (even
if it is impossible for it to end up in a superorganism)
provides, of its very nature, an aptitude, a predisposition, for receiving the Kingdom of God. This conten-
tion holds its own, and is of the first importance.

Mystical Body.[1] Evolution defines, as it were, a wish; it takes the first steps of the movement: but to reach the end of that movement calls for an energy and a love that Christ alone gives. The effects of that *predisposing* which (if we accept the theory of a natural superorganism) cosmogenesis contributed to the work of Christ, are now much more restricted, but something of them still remains; the laws of evolution urge us to unite, to grow in consciousness; and whatever follows this trend, serves the Pleroma.

But what becomes of the second "threshold of reflection" and "change of state" proclaimed by Teilhard? If we insist on retaining them, we are in the realm of hypothesis, for St. Paul says nothing of any such transformation.[2] I think one is well-advised in dropping such doubtful concepts altogether.

We shall, however, retain the idea of a total movement, whose interest should not be underestimated. The Mystical Body is the most

[1] Or again, a natural superorganism is implicit in the line of evolution, but the wounds left by original sin prevent our ever achieving it. Grace therefore takes on itself this added function which by rights should belong to nature. The view is allowable, but hypothetical. One wishes that Teilhard had explained himself on questions of such importance.

[2] The change of state of which Teilhard speaks is a change involving transition from the many to the new physical Person. It is not the same thing as the resurrection of the body.

wonderful assemblage of all, brought into being after prolonged evolution, which, in God's plan, was directed wholly towards it. It completes a movement whose successive stages were marked out by increasingly impressive achievements of complexity and consciousness; it confers on creation its highest degree of being and meaning, by establishing it in a supreme relationship with God.

I think it is of interest to return to the essential point—Teilhard's linking up of evolution and Christian perfection. There are many men of good will who do not accept St. Paul's ideas, or who wonder whether they are to be regarded as certain; but who nevertheless see Christian holiness as something of unquestionable value. To such men, provided they have a sense of the cosmos and of human history, Teilhard opens up far-reaching lines of thought.

Is it not possible that by being at last consciously in touch with the stuff of the universe we may come to find God in some quite special manner? In the East, it has always been thought that this was so; and although Eastern thought never wholly rid itself of elements of pantheism and naturalism, it is easier for us, with our heritage of Christian teaching, to avoid such accretions. Teilhard helps us to meet the cosmos and history in a movement which has God as its end; God in his supernatural mysteries; God in his fulness received, welcomed, through the course of evolution. The universe of itself is incapable of obtaining for us the gifts of God, but these gifts may be granted to us, or developed in us, by a complex process which makes use of the increase of consciousness of the evolutionary forces. It is more than a merely cerebral knowledge; it is a contact of the whole being with the totality of the forces of evolution.

We shall not make any headway unless we are really concerned to see right to the depths; if we confine ourselves to cosmic forces, without going beyond them, we shall not find God. We must seek out "*the* reality that men have always dimly felt behind things". "Being itself, as it came to dominate all the forms which it assumed, began to draw me and to intoxicate me."[1] Total being—also, then, and above all, ultimate being. I have reached the point where I ask myself, what is the real factor at work in evolution? It is not the universe alone, but its origin, its First Cause; and this is a divine will whose final aim is the salvation of mankind.

It is not enough to keep in mind the metaphysical depths of the evolving universe; these depths will only lead us to the Creator, not to the God who sanctifies. We must feel evolution as something leading up to the values of the Gospels, which are its goal. The rectifications that I have had earlier to make carry no weight against this argument—it is possible that the

[1] *M*, 119.

forces hitherto responsible for evolution will no
longer come into play; or, the idea of a superorganism runs us into insuperable difficulties—
and so on. But there has certainly been such a
phenomenon as evolution, carried still further
by the growth of humanity; and this general
history of life should be put at the service of
spiritual perfection. The force—ultimately, a
divine force—which determines evolutions is,
on this level, still at work; and it is completing
its task by giving supernatural gifts to men. It
is for us to get into touch with this force by seeking out its higher manifestations.[1]

Perhaps I may be allowed to put these
thoughts in a more concrete way—a way which
is no doubt open to argument and which only
certain temperaments will find helpful. But, if
the necessary modifications are made, it may
start some people off on a useful form of spiritual
exercise—one form; there are many others.

I get into a comfortable position, sitting down,
or, if I prefer it, lying down. I breathe slow,
deep, regular breaths. I feel the presence of
reality, like a force. Not just the universe, but,
at the source of the universe, ultimate reality;
fundamental reality. It is there, around me,
within me; it was already there, two thousand
years ago, in the days of the Romans, and further
back still; it is present everywhere, and to all
men. It is almost physically tangible in the sun,

[1] This plan of action is open to all, even unbelievers.

the rocks, the sea, the leaves, the air I breathe; and in the works of men. But it is power creating life, moving onward to its last end, far beyond these, as yet humble, manifestations. It calls me and bids me serve this end—take my part, an active part, in a love that is radiant, disinterested, creative—*agape*—that love with which God loves. I am asked to pass beyond my trifling, impure love to one that is glorious—that love whose traces I find in the universe, which tells me (if I am Christian enough to understand its voice aright) that they are but presages of what is to come.

And I can arrive at an intuitive consciousness of this supreme aim of creation—not, perhaps, by any association of concepts, but by keeping in my heart the pure, life-giving sap of the ideas so often discussed. And this sap is in me by the power that I see at work; I feel the cosmos like something ascending to the Kingdom of God, and receiving from him its full meaning.[1]

[1] A meaning which is infinitely beyond me. Reality is seen to be something distinct from my self, although I am steeped in it: but it is infinitely above me. I am soon in a state in which I can adore. It is not a question of becoming aware of my activity as a personal being, which seems so ludicrous. Nor is there any identification of nature with the divine (nor, incidentally, any technique of creating a mental vacuum, but simply of concentrating on what is most important). These objections, which are invariably (and often hastily) made against the methods of the East, do not apply here.

In this form of prayer, we take as a starting point our spontaneous wonder at the universe and life. We see in both a longing for completion; they are on their way somewhere ... darting towards ... towards some perfection where all the highest attributes of the spirit will be unfolded. As soon as we become conscious of belonging to a Whole, we feel an overwhelming interest linking us with the universe and its progress. The cosmos then becomes something quite different from all the little things round us, or our own little thoughts. It is like a breath, invisible, but giving life to everything. God is present there, as the origin and last end of evolution. The supernatural gifts are deeply desired, for God has destined them to crown the work now in progress; and we feel how much would be lacking if they were not there in all their fulness. And, what is far more, the work itself loses its importance in the face of God, the one focus, centre and origin of all that matters; the universe fades away, and the mystery of God (in his thought, in his love, in his life) stands forth as the one object to which we must cling. Evolution is a means of meditating on our end and desiring it in its integrity. An upward force—which is, ultimately, a sanctifying force —is here among us by reason of the very shape of life. The concrete nature, the extreme realism of this biological (biodynamic) perception makes it peculiarly well adapted to the mental outlook of our day.

And this perception takes on its full range if we realize the risk incurred: it is possible for mankind to miss the target. We should understand how empty human life becomes when the higher gifts of God are lacking. Evolution is then no longer seen as an invincible force, triumphantly accomplishing what it set out to do (this aspect alone would be misleading), but as something entrusted to human freedom and depending on that tenderness which God shows to man in spite of all his faults.

In short, any consideration of the cosmos and of history should have the effect of drawing us strongly towards the Christian virtues and the Kingdom of God (whatever name we may like to give it). This comes about in a very simple and direct way if our meditation on the Gospels is a matter of frequent occurrence, and if our lives as a whole are deliberately turned towards the spiritual. Then we are able to find God *in repose*, and in cleaving to our condition as truly and naturally as we can. The idea of God then ceases to be connected with a sense of constraint, with a kind of pious make-believe which often disappoints and sometimes worries us. Instead, we are borne to God by something vital, fundamental, something that comes from the very nature of things and of ourselves. We

8*

rediscover a whole forgotten mechanism—forgotten, or generally unknown: the praise of God, the waiting for his light; and we come to see that such activity is a true and normal function. We should make it our constant preoccupation to see that there is nothing impeding this function, throwing it out of gear. But on this point we have the traditional cautions of the spiritual life to enlighten us; it behoves us to know what they are.

It is, then, an excellent thing to pay heed to the forces of evolution, with the determination to lose nothing of their depth. The universe is ascending towards greater unity and consciousness, and, through this movement, God is preparing his Kingdom and his salvation. To pray means, always, to be in touch with the force that saves men. We must let this force take hold of us, do what it likes with us. There are some who know it best through evolution, for they see the cosmos as moving forward to the Gospel virtues. All that matters is that we should not confound the force that saves with any cosmic or human factor.

Thus understood, our prayer will, without any difficulty on our part, carry on in an unbroken line from our least religious activities. It is always the deep needs of the evolutionary movement (in other words, God's plan) which reveal themselves and call for effort from us. We have, collectively, a civilization to build up;

with Christ and for Christ we shall carry out the tasks that this great undertaking lays upon us. We know now; no marvelling over the world, no conquest of it, however Promethean, no collective ambitions, no temporal work of necessary revolution—none of all this runs counter to religion. It is partly thanks to Teilhard that we are able to see the providential harmony of the many elements making up our existence.

Yet there is still a practical problem to be solved. We are working with a tainted world. Are the means that it compels us to use in our dealings with it really in keeping with the supernatural ends that we are trying to serve? The danger lies in lulling our souls with harmonious theories and beautiful spiritual exercises while at the same time using means condemned by Christ. Against this danger there is no other weapon than a collective examination of conscience, carried out with all possible serenity, but with complete honesty of intention. The criticisms brought against us by unbelievers are often extremely enlightening. The problem will always be a searing one, for there is no perfect solution to it, but doubtless it is no bad thing for us to be slightly seared, if we are thereby roused from apathy over our real faults.

12

SHORT REFLECTIONS ON METHOD

THERE is one sentence in Teilhard's works which admirably sums up his attitude to the problems that interest him: "Let us resolutely adopt this line of thought. And let us try to follow it right to the end, to see where it leads us."[1] An idea comes to him, and seems very promising; he works it out with praise-worthy enthusiasm, pursuing the suggestions he sees in it to their extreme limit. Perhaps he is not quite critical enough of the results; such criticism is best applied after the idea has shown what is in it, if there is any fear of making it stillborn by an initial scrutiny that would lead to mistrust.

Teilhard thinks that he *understands* the meaning of evolution, and that this meaning is advance towards the greatest possible con-sciousness. Such an interpretation might be derived from Christian convictions (with the necessary modifications, it has a great deal to recommend it to the believer), but Teilhard claims to have deduced it from the study of

[1] *A*, 194.

cosmology itself. This shows a somewhat strange line of thought, which calls for a little notice. The example will help us to see Teilhard's methods and the whole drift of his conclusions; it will also show us how difficult—no doubt, impossible—it is to avoid making certain arbitrary decisions in any thinking done within the field of biology.

It is instructive to compare the *established data* with the *conclusions drawn from them*.

The established data are: the succession of forms, which become increasingly complex; the appearance and growth of psychism, at least in certain branches; and consciousness, properly so called, at the tip of one shoot, and one alone—ours.

The conclusions drawn: A cosmogenesis comparable with the development of an embryo, and culminating in the hyper-personalized human world of the future, just as the embryo ends up as the completed organ. We may leave to one side all that concerns the humanity of the future; the interpretation of evolution up to its present stage gives us quite enough to think about. Teilhard believes in an *evolutionary unity* of the universe—that all things are converging to the same end—and that this end is the highest possible degree of consciousness.

He has, then, discovered *the* phenomenon, the law, the key to the universe, the true axis of evolution. The nerve centre of his exposition is no doubt the point where he seeks the true parameter—in other words, the variable element enabling us to assess objectively the degree attained, at a given stage, by evolutionary progress. It seemed natural to him to take as his measure the degree of complexity; let us grant this, although there is already a choice involved; and this choice would only be entirely justified if complexity were beyond all doubt the specific effect of the forces at work (about which we as yet know very little). But "how are we to assess the *comparative* complexities of plant and polyp, of insect and vertebrate, of reptile and mammal"?[1] The answer is: By the brain. The parameter of cephalization must undoubtedly be the right one. Why? Because of the following argument: "That which, at every point and every instant, defines and measures the involution of the universe, is, by definition, the degree of vitalization reached by matter at the point and summit under consideration."[2] We are then told that complexity and vitalization are equivalent terms, and that the measure of both is given by consciousness, or interiorization, or "psychical temperature".

It is therefore asserted:

(1) that the universe is undergoing one single process of involution, one single genesis, as coherent as a brilliant thought:

[1] *G,* 56.   [2] *G,* 56.

(2) that this genesis is that of psychical forces, carried to the highest degree.

The second of these ideas follows if we grant the first; for, if the universe is tending to one end, it probably is its mission to cause new powers to appear in matter; and, of these new powers, the most characteristic are those of psychism. But underlying all this there is an implicit option. Let us try to see what it is; we are imagining a cosmic convergence of the same type as the human idea.

We have begun by assuming that there is unity and coherence in the modifications of life that occur. The very idea of a parameter, in the sense in which Teilhard speaks of it, implies this assumption. If life fuses in all directions, if there is not, beyond all the intricacy of the branches, one single ascent, where would be the point of speaking of a single parameter? We are assuming *an* advance, and so we seek *a* criterion. But what is really happening has to be put in the conditional tense; *were* the universe in a state of convergence, what *would* be the criterion of the degree of convergence attained?

It will be said that all the evidence points to the belief that the world is becoming interiorized; that—at least in our biosphere—it is undergoing an increasingly marked transformation, culminating in thinking man. This is indeed a convergence, but there are convergences of very different types; and herein lies the whole problem. Let us for a moment adopt the hypothesis of "advanced" action: we now have a convergence of a relatively obvious kind. It involves the application of a single parameter; at a given moment, the entire universe (or at any rate the entire field of action) is in advance on its previous states and nearer the pole where all will be co-ordinated. The simplest criterion, in that case, is time; yet local setbacks may lead to complications and delays; so that it is natural to try to find some criterion applicable to the result attained. Complexity is then the best parameter, if the specific effect of "advanced" action is an improbable structure. In this case, complexity is not, in the first place, interiority or psychism, but improbability. Is the degree of cephalization an accurate means of measurement? This is by no means clear, and the question calls for further discussion. Teilhard has opted for saying that any form of complexity other than cephalization is purely accidental, and doesn't count. Of the three great branches on the tree of life, two—the vegetable kingdom and the arthropods[1]—can be summarily dismissed; they do not end up in a brain.

Among the extremely varied results produced by the universe, we make a choice; we *note what matters.* But when we look into the question of what matters, do we mean anything that hap-

[1] See G, 47 for the tree of life drawn up by Teilhard.

pens to speak to our own minds, or what we should have done if we had been in charge of the world, or an objective fact? Is our preference dictated to us by reality? Does it correspond with the true pivot of the cosmos?

If we really knew what the forces of evolution were, we should be able to deduce from them their specific effects. Without this knowledge, we are all too like the spectator who imagines that the purpose of a magnetic field is to produce decorative patterns.[1] In actual fact, we do not know for certain the systematic factor (if there is one) equivalent to evolutionary "gravity". Consequently, we cannot know what its specific effect is; the most we can do is try to gauge it by looking at results. It seems, then, impossible, at the present stage of scientific knowledge, to find a purely objective criterion— a criterion, that is, containing no element of interpretation on our part.

Ever since Nietzsche, existentialist thought has shown (with occasional exaggerations) how natural it is to us, when we look at things, to assess or interpret them: it is a tendency closely connected with that vital choice which makes up our being, projecting it into the future. Such a process is, I think, undoubtedly inseparable from human thought, and we see it at work in Teilhard when he defines evolution as an advance towards consciousness. Science should, as

[1] See above, pp. 122–3.

far as possible, eliminate the subjective element; therein lies its honesty. But there always comes a time when the scientist has said the last word of what he knows, and the man takes over to provide the explanation; and this he does by making his own assessments, based indeed on reason, but going beyond the established facts. In Teilhard's case, this time comes very soon; what he offers us is a sort of existentialist science, which is certainly interesting; but one should know what one is about, and in general scientists are on another track.[1] Pure positivism is, no doubt, impossible, especially in biology; the mind outruns the known facts; if it did not, it would lose its zest; but it should do what it can to obtain proofs.

Teilhard's method is somewhat reminiscent of a wager. To begin with he assumes that, despite the diversity of mechanisms, there is a single law throughout evolution, just as there is a single group of formulae—the Lorenz Equations—on which all relativity is based.[2] Then he

[1] Teilhard does, however, stick to the general concept of science in his technical works on palaeontology, especially those treating of human fossils.

[2] The unifying law here in question relates to cultural human evolution, but in so far as it "represents the direct prolongation and accentuation of the general phenomenon of organic evolution". What is finally envisaged, as defining the "evolutionary unity of the universe", is the law of advance towards the highest degree of consciousness.

grants, by implication, that the human mind is able to find an adequate definition of this law, not by examining physical mechanisms, but by a general, intuitive appreciation of the results. It is this type of appreciation which seems to me at once interesting and extra-scientific. Teilhard thinks he has hit on the working orders directing evolution. It is evident to him that the universe is undergoing a process, not only of self-concentration, but of interiorization; this is an idea which "speaks" to the human mind—just such an idea as we might ourselves have had. Here, then, is what justifies his choice of the parameter of cephalization: by it "the confused jungle-growth, the crowd of living things, grows clear and orderly, and finally shoots up, in a single rush and following the line of one main branch".[1] Yes, in all science an hypothesis which gives greater coherence to established facts, and which opens a new field for action, has some chance of being true, or at least of expressing a truth, however inadequately it may as yet be formulated. But is what we have here the same coherence, the same fecundity, that we usually seek from science? Einstein's theory, while retaining what is true in Newtonian mechanics, brings into line facts that had long been known, and recently acquired facts which seemed to be at loggerheads with them; it unifies aspects of

[1] G, 58.

reality which appeared irreconcilable. The unification effected by this theory concerns the same group of quantitative relations; and we know that the universe is governed by relations of this nature. But the intelligible regrouping of evolutionary phenomena by a law of unity and consciousness presupposes a sort of half-human intention running through the universe; and we have good reason to think that, up to a fairly recent period, the universe contained nothing of the kind. In speaking of the *meaning* of evolution we run the risk, as has already been said, of juggling with words and arguing in a circle. Three types of procedure are open to us, of which one—the second—is extremely risky.

We may speak of the cosmos itself, in which case, while noting the direction of its progress, we have no right to infer anything that resembles an intention.

Or we may allow the human mind to transcribe the facts in its own medium, that of thought and action; we let these facts set up echoes in the human mind; we speak as if the cosmos were a factory carrying out a schedule; we find a human equivalent for cosmic acts; we draw up a humanoid plan which corresponds roughly, if not in every detail, with the process of evolution. But we should realize that the transposition is purely fictitious.

Or, finally, we may have in mind the plan of a Creator; in which case we ought to say so.

It is true that, if we accept Teilhard's explanation, living things as a whole do seem to grow more intelligible, more ordered, more progressive. This may have its value, if what we are looking for is an apologetic argument; but if we are thinking scientifically, this very fact should put us on our guard; are the procedures of the cosmos such as satisfy our minds *in this way*? The intelligibility which the law of unity and consciousness reveals to us is of a very special type; it is not only that which brings order into our knowledge; it is, above all, that which orders it according to a plan—and this suggests an aim. Not so much in that it resembles human reason (like a system of equations, which may be the law of the *object* of our intelligence), but in that it resembles human *existence*, the drive to the future. Now, I do not believe that any such law could (before man's day) belong to the cosmos as such; and certain passages in Teilhard's writings acknowledge this; psychism, at the beginning, could only account for an extremely small part of evolutionary "gravity". Hence, in describing the facts as the realization of a plan, we are studying the cosmos with thought superadded to it—our own thought, or God's.

The law of complexity-consciousness can only be if we read anthropomorphic significance into reality. Now, the specific effect of physical causes (even on the hypothesis of "advanced" action) is not of this nature. The law of complexity-consciousness is not, then, derived from science. Does it derive from a *philosophy* of biology? This would be its natural place, but we must think carefully about this.

Teilhard is saying, not only that evolution produces consciousness or psychism (which no one would question), but that the rise of consciousness represents the whole trend of the advance of evolution. For this idea to be justified, there would have to be an anthropomorphic necessity *in the cosmos*—not in the mind of God or in our own. Scientifically speaking, the rise of consciousness appears as a local effect, comparable with a statistical effect—the result, that is to say, of a great many chances: if there is any necessity about it, this is not apparent.[1] We should still have to discover a cosmic aim that was intelligible in the total (anthropomorphic) sense that Teilhard takes for granted. Aristotle would have tried to demonstrate that there was such an aim, and perhaps it is possible to do so, if one adopts the Aristotelian notion of a final cause. But in fact any talk of finality in biology is apt to be misleading, and I think that,

[1] The syntropic wave brings us very near it. But—quite apart from the caution with which scientists now regard this theory—there still remain all the problems raised by the identification of improbability and consciousness.

until the existence of a Mind has been established, we should avoid the word "end". If we use another vocabulary (other concepts) and feel our way very cautiously and with sufficient penetration, we need not rule out the possibility of defining a convergence more or less comparable with human design. But this approximation needs careful handling. The most, doubtless, that we shall ever establish is a convergence of the same type as that of "advanced" actions, which does not lead to consciousness as such. We must, then, ponder the significance of the facts as they present themselves to the mind, and ask ourselves what explanation can be found for them.

We are finally faced with the following dilemma:

Either the world produces consciousness in more or less the same way as the magnetic spectrum produces decorative patterns—in which case the advance of consciousness is not *the* law, *the* essential phenomenon (and the future of consciousness remains uncertain):

Or—whatever mechanism may be at work, whatever may be the nature of evolutionary forces and of their specific effect—consciousness is systematically produced. To accept this solution probably means admitting the existence of God.

I do not think that any purely *scientific* observation permits of a choice between the two concepts. And this is where Teilhard may mislead us. The choice is strictly philosophical, and can only be made after long and extremely arduous study, carried out by appropriate methods, on the philosophical level.

Teilhard is, in fact, swayed to some extent by his religious convictions. It is they that lead him to think that the cosmos produces consciousness systematically. In the long run, he is right, if God exists. But he is only right on the whole. His description of the fact of evolution is not, as he claims, scientific; if we are to accept the law of complexity-consciousness, we have to go beyond the study of mechanisms and find a significance that has no immediate connection with physical causes and their effects—a significance concerning which we are not on very sure ground. Teilhard then goes on to deduce highly debatable consequences from this law—the superorganism, the infallibility of the drive towards consciousness, the existence of God as a condition of its success.

Yet, even when we have made these reservations, Teilhard's intuitions do, to a great extent, come off. Not only does the passage of time cause psychical progress to appear, but life culminates, in man, in a network of characteristics nowhere else obtained. "During the last two million years, we may observe innumerable disappearances; but nothing really new, with the exception of the hominoids, has appeared in nature." "What vitality, what exuberance, what originality there is in this last-born of earth's children!"[1] Mankind, in addition to its powers of expansion and swift differentiation, has the ability to form into groups, to envelop our planet in a "completely new covering".[2] This is a fact which must perforce be recognized. When Teilhard links in one series the formation of corpuscles and spiritual phenomena, he does not connect the mechanisms sufficiently closely; but he has none the less discovered a great reality. Thus intuition reaches the mark, and there is something to be said for the means adopted. At the very least, it shows us a group of facts which are important *to us*.

To the scientist, this method is suspect, partial and annoying. The philosopher is distressed by the lack of detail, which seems to him almost irresponsible. To the ordinary man, the results are striking, astonishingly expressive, and (partly) true.

Beyond all the uncertainties of science, beyond the cautious procedure of rational method, there is doubtless scope for the penetrating gaze which discovers before it can prove. This is Teilhard's aim: to coincide with what is, in fact, the intelligible movement of the universe, The conclusion to be drawn implies the existence of

[1] G, 93.   [2] G, 107.

God; and this Teilhard knows. He is anticipating the proof. His whole thought is focused on a certain significance within cosmic reality—a significance which, in the final analysis, would appear to point to a divine plan. His legitimation will follow as and when proof of these things is forthcoming; and even if the demonstration can never be conclusive, the intelligibility of the results will itself furnish us with an argument. These are not the methods of science; the whole train of reasoning is discreetly theological, for Christian belief enters into it. Even a pagan may be impressed: he will not, it is true, be given any irrefutable evidence, but he will find himself wondering whether he has not, after all, been shown the true law of reality; and the raising of this question will do more than anything to awaken his mind.

I do not think that Teilhard lays himself open to the charge of using science as a camouflage for what is really theological. He starts off from two points, draws his inspiration from two sources—both, to him, equally valid. He is quite sincere in his attempt to make science account for everything within its range; when hypotheses become necessary, he at once (and without always seeing that he is interpreting without proof) chooses the explanation that accords with his Christian beliefs.

The most serious criticism that can be made of his thought is provoked by its methodological confusion. He is trying to gain a complete view of the world from science, by following up one single line of thought. Now, such procedure may be all very well at the stage of discovery, but later on one has to keep far more strictly within the various disciplines—philosophy of science, philosophy, theology; and each order has methods peculiar to it. While the philosophy of sciences may well take over from physics or biology, a complete change of method becomes necessary as soon as one moves on to philosophy in the true sense of the word. It is then no longer enough to extend the results in a rough way; new understanding—the result of 2,500 years of hard thinking—should come into play; above all, one must understand the specific workings of the mind, its position as regards its object, and the way in which the object reveals its meanings.

The findings of science (even if one uses the word in an extended sense, to cover the wide field of its philosophy) cannot tell us all there is to know about the meaning of life, how man should behave, his attitude to reality, or the metaphysical structure of reality itself. But we can start off from science, and make it our basis for a development of progressive speculation containing no element of option—or, where option is inevitable, in full awareness of our choices, and able to justify them. At certain stages we shall need new methods and new lights, and an entirely new mental training. I believe, moreover, that metaphysics has to be transcended, for it is inadequate as a source of spiritual life; and our transition into the order of religion raises its own problems, just as our entry into the metaphysical order confronted us with other problems peculiar to metaphysics.

The methods vary in technique, but the quest is always the same; what we are seeking throughout is truth in thought and action.

13

THE PLAN OF WORK

THOSE who condemn Teilhard should try to go one better; they should start by sharing with him, and in the same degree, his secret perceptions of contemporary thought—thought which is new and living. Whatever his shortcomings, Teilhard attains a kind of objectivity, a peculiar rightness, through certain outstanding qualities which we should try to learn from him.

The first of these is generosity of spirit. The value of his thought is not diminished by any personal mediocrity; his mind is never made barren by prejudice, rancour, narrowness of sympathy or pettiness of choice.

Then, breadth of vision. He is interested, in an extremely personal way, in every aspect of life; not only in the various forms of science which set out to probe the universe, but in the works and hopes of man, and the profound life of the spirit.

Next, technical competence on a wide scale.[1] Teilhard practises "knowledge by connaturality",

[1] Except as regards philosophical reflection or theology.

brought about by his communing with, and meditation on, nature. He uses the training of a specialist to perfect his intuitive grasp of reality. He is in a bond of living sympathy with the universe; he catches its undertones, his imagination is full of it—which is why, even when we question it, we catch in it the echoes of truth.

He has shown us many promising spots to dig in; above all, he has a sense (and he is one of few to have it) of what, in science, may contain spiritual values; and this, today, interests us to the highest degree. He does not dig deep enough; his conclusions are of the hit-or-miss type—and this, despite the fact that discipline of thought is, precisely, of considerable spiritual value. It is for us to take up the same great themes, but with a stricter control. He declares that his vision cannot remain stationary[1]; it must, like a living thing, improve; and it is our task to turn this vision on to what will attain his purpose more completely.

Teilhard suffers from not having given careful study to the other alternative—the alternative which did not correspond to his own spontaneous impulse. He should have confronted his ideas, over a long period, with the fundamental intuitions of Christianity, and sought competent help in doing so. Even on the philosophical level he certainly ought to have left more room for

[1] *P*, 300.

contradiction, the negative, the tragic. His thought would have gained in depth if it had made more explicit the element of contingency in evolutionary development and the human growth of spirit, and if it had dealt with the problems raised by "crossing" the various thresh-holds. Man's open assumption of his functions as a spiritual being did not take place without a struggle[1]; in the same way, the moment we set out resolutely on the road of religious enquiry, we are beset by a swarm of theoretical and con-crete problems hardly touched on in *Le Milieu divin*—which have the effect of making the blos-soming forth of science into spiritual life any-thing but simple and idyllic.

But what Teilhard has left undone, others may finish for him. It is quite likely that nothing but team work, combining at least a true scien-tist, a true philosopher and a true theologian—will be able to throw sufficient light on the difficult questions which Teilhard attacked with such almost artless confidence. He certainly underestimated their difficulties. It is to be hoped that careful teams will study, not only the questions dealt with by Teilhard de Char-din, but all those which extend the frontiers of science, and which, with science as their start-ing-point, lead on to humanism and wisdom.

[1] Whatever the truth may be about an ontological break; the conflicts that arise are within the order of phenomena.